THE BEE-BOOK BOOK

The "Humane" Bee-Hive.

Ephemeral engraving of 1866 "The British Workman".

"This good man can tell much about the bees – their way of life, their industry, their skill, and their uses in God's world. He has kept bees for a long time.... and has read trustworthy books about them."

THE BEE-BOOK BOOK

A Manual for Collectors

by

GEOFFREY LAWES

NORTHERN BEE BOOKS

Published 1991 by:
Northern Bee Books
Scout Bottom Farm
Mytholmroyd, Hebden Bridge,
West Yorks. HX7 5JS

ISBN O 907908 57 8

Photographs and illustrations by the author.

Typesetting by:
Anne Lister Typesetting, Halifax.

Designed & Printed by:
Arc & Throstle Press, Todmorden.

Contents

Illustrations

1.
The Scope and Purpose of the Collecting Impulse

Just as beekeepers may name a thousand motives for embracing the dangerous mystery of apiculture, so the bee-book bibliophile indulges his fancy for the literature of the craft for many diverse reasons. The apiarist may keep a single colony, or allow his hives to proliferate beyond his means to service them. Likewise the collector may maintain a modest shelf of special texts, or allow his hunger for books to grow into an insatiable obsession.

Almost every collector can trace his initial interest to curiosity and a quest for knowledge. He buys his first books to learn more of the secrets of the bees. All bee writers through the ages have struggled to set down their knowledge for the information and delight of their beekeeper readers. They teach the craft and celebrate the pleasure of the art of keeping bees. Each new book published is destined to grow obsolete with the passage of time. But every new work may state or restate a timeless truth or an exciting idea with freshness, clarity, pictorial skill or descriptive power unequalled by earlier authors.

The beekeeper with many books has mastery, without time-consuming research, of the best that is known of the fascinating insect handily stored in his personal library. Book-learning divorced from practice may be sterile, but bee-lore won by practice alone is tedious and slow, narrowly limited by the capabilities, insights and resources of each individual practitioner. Good books supercharge good practice, boosting it with the collected wisdom of experts living and dead throughout the world.

Scientists, beefarmers, brilliant hobbyists, poets, artists and philosophers, all have kept bees down the ages and passed on their insights to posterity through the printed word. The bee-book collector is the custodian of that heritage. Just as the authors felt impelled to set down the best that they knew in words and pictures, so the collector should embrace his duty to care for the word-hoard, as the Anglo Saxons called it. Books are the treasure chest of bee culture and every good collection should be preserved with loving attentiveness as a donation from the past to the future.

An example of the philanthropy of a series of bibliophiles is related by the late Harrison Ashforth, himself an eminent beekeeper and bookman.

William Tegetmeier was born in 1816. He was remarkable for introducing both pigeon racing and Langstroth's discovery of the bee-space into Britain. He was a prolific journalist in 'Field' and 'The Queen' on natural history matters, a poultry breeder, a fierce opponent in newspaper controversies of Dr. John Cumming, the 'Times Bee-master', a skilful beekeeper who improved the Stewarton hive and the author of 'Bees, Hives and Honey'(1860). He also collected bee books.

He sold them to Alfred Neighbour, the hive maker who, with T. W. Woodbury introduced Italian queens into England.

Neighbour wrote a best-seller, 'The Apiary' in 1865. When he died in 1890 Col.H.J.O. Walker bought his collection as the nucleus of his own superb library. He, in turn, sold it to the Miller library in Wisconsin USA in 1930. Without these three remarkable collectors Western scholarship would be immeasurably the poorer.

The bee-book library is not only a source of up-to-date information, but it is also a chronological record of the history of the craft. Successive dated books spell out the evolution of knowledge. By quotation and reference the beekeeping historian can derive a precise account of progress. By research for example, he might find the first reference to Isle of Wight disease to pinpoint its identification in Britain, or trace the history of foul brood, or chart the introduction and popularisation of moveable frame hives in the nineteenth century.

Future generations will be grateful for those who knew bee-books to be historical documents and collected them privately to augment the work of the world's great libraries. (A list of such great public collections is appended as a footnote).

Of equal importance to the exposition of the history of the craft is the record of the natural history of the honey bee itself. From Hooke (1665) through van Leewenhoek (1673), Swammerdam (1758), Cheshire (1886), Cowan (1890), Nelson (1915), Annie Betts (1923), Herrod-Hempsall (1938), Snodgrass (1956) and Dade (1962) can be traced the story of bee anatomy as revealed by the light microscope. In due course the wonderful revelations of the electron microscope will be published too.

The field of view continues to widen as the collector turns his attention to other bee-related matters of absorbing interest to apiarists. Books on pollination,bee plants,honey cookery, wax and its uses, bee houses, other bees and wasps, bee diseases, the world honey trade, honey farming and economics, the medical applications of honey, royal jelly pollen and venom, close-up photography, bees in prehistory and the classics, art, poetry, folklore, films, social history and philosophy all find a worthy place on the book shelves of the true enthusiast.

It is for these many reasons that bee books are rarely to be found gathering dust on the shelves of second-hand book dealers.

Famous Public Collections

British Library, London, WCIB 3DG
IBRA, Cardiff.
Trinity College, Dublin 2.
Ministry of Agriculture Library, London.
Hereford and Worcester, Hereford.
University of Reading, RG6 2AG.
Bodleian, Oxford, OX1 3BG.
Rothamsted Experimental Station, Harpenden.
Moir Library (Scottish B.K.A.) Edinburgh EH1 1EG.
University of Cambridge, CB3 9DR.
Mann Library, Cornell University (New York)
Miller Library, Univ. of Wisconsin.
Library of Congress, Washington D.C.
See 'British Bee Books' pps. 21-3 for detailed information.

2.
The Range of Beekeeping Books

Book collectors must discipline themselves to a carefully defined field of interest. If the chosen subject is too wide, even though the collector may have unlimited leisure, the riches of Croesus and a warehouse, he may still find his pastime to be a burden to him. The scholar who sets out to write a short thesis on the history of ideas in the western world may soon come to wish that he had opted for something within his compass like the reasons a miller wears a white hat! So it is with collecting books. Some topics embraced by specialist collectors - gardening, birds, cookery, old school books and so forth - are practicable only in sub-divisions. Farming books, for example, are too large a topic, but a sub-section such as, say nineteenth century books on sheep or farriery up to 1800 would provide a controllable framework for a sensible collection. Most topics prove to be enormous in scope with legions of authors world-wide. The collector preserves his sanity by concentrating on an aspect, an area or a period of the whole subject.

Books on bees are not exceptional in this regard. To collect the bee books of the world in all languages, or even in English, throughout the period of the printed word would be a challenge too daunting for any sapient being.

The canon of British bee books, as listed in the authoritative bibliography "British Bee Books 1500-1976" by the International Bee Research Association, lists 832 book entries. A great many more titles have been published since 1976. This is a conceivable target, even though that figure would be significantly increased because many titles exist in various editions sufficiently different to make them independently collectable. It is, however, an unattainable goal because many of the items listed are believed to exist in only a single copy – but again the pursuit of rarity is the headiest wine of the connoisseur! To collect all the available books published in Britain up to 1976 might be possible by the power of the purse to command the ownership of other collections, but it would be a lifetime's task by the honest route of book by book accumulation. Pleasure lies in the detection of the quarry and the excitement of the chase as much as in possession itself.

The British bee-book collector, unless very strong willed, is bound to acquire volumes published in the U.S.A. Some American authors, for example Snodgrass, Morse and Teale, will have English publishers and so fall within the canon of British bee-books. But to collect both British and American books would be an act of bravado. Other English language imports, Australian and New Zealand for instance, or books on tropical beekeeping where English is used as a 'lingua franca', can all extend the range of possibilities.

It is for the collector to impose his own limits. These could take many forms. Some might collect books in other languages – French, German or Italian. Each such European language except Russian accounts for only 5% of known books, according to Eva Crane. Others might concentrate on only the most recent books in all languages at the sharp edge of knowledge. Others again might put down a final marker at 1850 and collect only antiquarian books in all languages up to that date. Yet others might focus on all the books written about a particular region of the world - Sussex, East Anglia, Wales, or New Zealand for example. Some might limit their collection to all books first published in the nineteenth century in English – British, American and colonial. Possibilities are numerous, but firm parameters are a sensible discipline, helping to preserve sanity and to save marriages and shelf-space.

3.
Bibliography

Bibliography is writing about books, and can be considered under three headings. First is enumerative bibliography. This is making lists of books for particular purposes, such as helpful reference books or lists of books for consultation or further reading. Such lists occasionally appear in bee books. W.C. Cotton in 'My Bee Book' (1842) lists nine pages of authors on bee subjects. To recreate this list might be a superb project for a collector! Another example would be the list of books recommended by the IBRA for examination candidates to read. ('Bee World' 1966 Vol.47). The 'Illustrated Encyclopedia of Beekeeping' by Morse and Hooper, 1985, lists 17 titles of essential reading and the names of authors reckoned important.Maeterlinck's 'The Life of the Bee' carries a splendid international list of "more interesting work," which he has used.

Analytical bibliography deals with the processes, the ways and means, of getting the author's original manuscript into printed form.

Descriptive bibiography, which the bee book collector uses, draws on analysis, but fundamentally it describes the physical properties of a book or a series of similar books. Bibliographers are not deeply concerned with the intellectual contents of books. Questions of style, meaning, literary or scientific importance are left to the critics. Descriptive bibliographers do care about the characteristics of books as physical objects that have been printed, bound and decorated. They describe as accurately as they can the artefact we should expect to hold in our hand which is alleged to be such-and-such edition of so-and-so's book called by such-and-such a title of a particular likely date of issue.

Many, but by no means all specialist subjects have their own descriptive bibliographies. Bee book collectors are most fortunate in that "British Bee Books – A Bibliography 1500 – 1976" published in 1979 is an exceptionally valuable work. It describes accurately every British publication of that period on bees, together with general works which have more than twenty pages on bees. It also lists manuscript (i.e. handwritten) documents prior to 1500 and books which make metaphorical reference to bees. The various indexes are particularly helpful categorising separately, for example, books in verse, works of fiction and children's books. There is a short title index, an author index and an index of special sub-topics such as mead-making and bee diseases.

Every title is assigned an entry or reference number which dealers often quote in their catalogues or correspondence for easy reference by their customers. No doubt in due course the IBRA will commission a supplement to update the bibliography from 1976 to the present.

Amongst much other descriptive information the bibliography gives:

1. i. Author's name and style (Rev, Dr, etc)
   ii. Entry - or reference number.
   iii. Date.

2. i. Short title (in italics) then the rest of the title.
   ii. Place of publication and publisher.
   iii. Date.
   iv. No. of pages - roman numerals for preliminary pages – arabic numerals for main text and numbers of relevant pages if the book has only a section on bees.
   v. Detail of frontispiece and plates, and in some cases of illustrations. (The bibliography is imprecise in this respect).
   vi. Whether the book has its own bibliography.
   vii. One or more capital letters to indicate famous libraries holding a copy.
   e.g. A - British Library.
   B - IBRA Library.
   S - Moir Library. [Only B or an alternative is noted after 1927]
   viii. Page height (if not between 16 and 24 cms)

3. Details of later editions (but not on books only partly on bees)

4. Cross references to entry numbers in other bibliographies (up to 1927 only, except for Hodgson [children] and Johansson [USA]).

5. Notes of interest, usually about the author or printing and publication, but occasionally about the intellectual content of the work and the author's contribution to bee knowledge [not many after 1927]

[Square brackets in the bibliography mean that the information in question is derived from sources outside the book itself. .?. indicates uncertainty.]

The collector should also be acquainted with certain other useful bibliographies which dealers and experts use. This is a brief list.

Cole:	'The Cole Library of Early Medicine and Zoology' by N.B. Eales. University of Reading 1969.
G. Fussell	'The Old English Farming Books 1523-1730' 'More Old Farming Books 1731-1793' Crosby Lockwood 1947 and 1950.

	Dr. George Fussell died in Jan 1990 aged over 100 years.
B. Henrey	'British Botanical and Horticultural Literature before 1800' 3 Volumes. OUP 1975.
N.B. Hodgson	Children's Books on Bees and Beekeeping. Bee Research Assoc. 1973.
Johansson (T.S.K. & M.P)	Apicultural Literature published in Canada and the United States 1972 (Available from IBRA)
Lisney A.A.	On butterflies and moths. 'A bibliography of British Lepidoptera 1608 - 1799' (1960).
Plomer H.R.	A dictionary of the printers and booksellers in England, Scotland and Ireland. 4 Volumes 1977.
S.T.C.	'A Short Title Catalogue' - of British books 1475 to 1640. Reprinted 2 volumes by London Bibliographical Society A-H 1986, I-Z 1976.
Wing D.	Continues on from S.T.C. 'Short Title Catalogue' – of books in English throughout the world from 1641 to 1700, 3 vols. (D. Wing, Index Society 1945).

Other Useful Works.

Fraser H.M.	History of Beekeeping in Britain (Bee Research Assoc. 1958)
Moir.	Catalogue of the Moir Library (Scottish B.K.A.) 1950 With supplement to 1962.
Walker H.J.O.	Descriptive Catalogue - bee books offered for sale by Lt.Col.H.J.O. Walker, 1929. Northern Bee Books reprint 1985.
Cotton W.C.	'My Bee Book' 1842. Kingsmead reprint 1970.
Dodds V.	'Beemasters of the Past' Northern Bee Books 1983.
Mace H.	'Bee matters and Bee Masters' 1st edition 1930. Appendix "Who's who in beekeeping" lists. 125 prominent beekeepers of his day.
IBRA (Dawson)	'Index of Apicultural Abstracts 1952 -1972' 2 volumes. Lists 14,424 publications worldwide

representing the work of 7000 authors. This material is computer generated.

'International Book Catalogue' – a helpful if not exhaustive list of books available from IBRA.

'Bee World Index 1919 - 1949' lists books reported in the text of 'Bee World'

Collectable books in German, French and Italian.

'Apicultural Abstracts' in good company.

French Books

Bibliographie d'apiculture de langue francaise (in French)
C. de Casteljan. Lists 1607 books.

The bee-book bibliography 'British Bee Books' is the collector's main tool. As a beginner it is his teacher, his map to the territory, guiding him to a basic knowledge of authors and their work. It defines what is a bee book and what is not, and helps him place the major books in time.

When the day comes for the collector to buy, and eventually to sell, then the descriptive bibliography is his essential guide. He will need to answer four questions about any book he proposes to buy:

1. Is the book complete?

2. What is its date?

3. Are the plates and illustrations all present?

4. What relationship does this copy have with other copies of the same edition, or other editions of the same work?

The good bibliography helps in all four respects. It arms the customer with knowledge about his potential purchase. Without that knowledge he is defenceless against sharp practice.

The answer to the questions will not be fully supplied without a thorough scrutiny of the book itself as will be explained later.

4.
Books as an Investment

Since the Second World War there has been a revolution in our attitude to the goods and chattels of our forebears. Post-war junk shops selling relics of the past at knock-down prices have been superseded by antiques emporia run by well-heeled entrepreneurs, often with a flourishing shipping trade to outlets overseas.

There is a world-wide thirst for honest, handmade, nostalgic artefacts which predate modern materials and mass-production. Such objects inevitably become fewer with the passage of time. Affluent romantics with a yearning for things past become more acquisitive. As supply shrinks and demand grows, so prices rise. Quality items, well preserved and over fifty years old, prove to be better investments than money in the building society.

Antiquarian books bear up well as investments. Lt. Col. H.J.O. Walker's catalogue of his library of bee books published in 1929 quoted various editions of Butler's 'Feminine Monarchie' at about £2 and Swammerdam's 'The Book of Nature' at £1. The present value of such books would be about £500. The catalogue is interesting in showing the value of one collectable book compared with another. But it also demonstrates what a splendid hedge against inflation good books have been after a lapse of sixty years.

Inflation is indexed at "x 25" from 1930 to 1990. By this measure a £1 book would now be worth only £25. This is slightly less than what £1 invested at 5% in 1930 at compound interest would be worth today, less tax. Investment in a house and garden in 1930 would have been a good inflation-beater, but 200 one hundred year old bee books would now be more valuable and would have been cheaper to maintain and insure. One cannot live in old books, or rent them out, but they have a beauty superior to domestic bricks and mortar.

William Rees-Mogg in an article in "The Independent" newspaper revealed increases in old book dollar prices between 1901 and 1990 varying between 200 times for a set of the four folios of Shakespeare, 100 times for Samuel Johnson's letters, 75 times for Wordsworth's poems, 37 times for Izaak Walton's 'lives' and 26 times for Pope's 'Dunciad'. Gold rose in price 18 times in the same period. Antiquarian books have, at worst kept pace with inflation and more fashionable titles have risen in value by 10 times in real terms.

For a while second-hand books lagged behind the booming antique business and were bought and sold relatively cheaply. In the first two post-war decades it was possible to acquire windfall stocks from general dealers and country house auctions. Such days are long past. Bookfinders and dealers now mobilize to scrutinise all possible remaining hoards. Slick fingers delve amongst the book table at jumble sales, but major hauls are a rarity. Good books are no longer sold at giveaway prices. The book trade has organised itself to match demand. Prices are high. There is a shortage of stock so that at book fairs and auctions book dealers often buy and sell to one another. The libraries of old rectories have all been plundered. The hungry booksellers look up, and are not fed.

Meantime the book trade has diversified. Specialist traders have emerged to cater for every particular type of collector. There are specialists in girls' school stories, science fiction, gardening, horror and what-you-will. There are, at the time of writing, three major mail order dealers in bee books and several natural history specialist bookshops which keep a bee list. The inevitable result is that general second hand bookshops are denied the better stock because of the power of the purse of the specialist buyer. General shops rarely harbour collectable titles for long. Browsing can be unrewarding, for good bee books are hard to find, and scarce commodities attract legions of book hunters with an eye to business. With the passage of time fragile artefacts like books subject to fire, flood, insects, children's wax crayons and careless custodians become rarer by the day. The world market grows larger. Prices continue to rise.

Books are quite easy to store. A few fine bookcases stocked with handsome volumes are a joy to find in a well-appointed home. Insurance is cheap, burglary unlikely, maintenance minimal and a labour of love to the aficionado.

Buy books and instruct your heirs in their worth. If you are the parent of Philistines teach them their price. In neither case will they be disappointed.

It is worth remembering that in theory a collection of books when

Old books on display.

New books and duplicates on open shelves.

sold together has an enhanced value over the constituent volumes priced separately. But a collection sold complete means that one buyer has to find the whole price. Selling the books individually enables the seller to gather the purchase money from many different sources, with scope for some higher prices.

5.
Book Collecting 'Know-How'
i

Collectors must acquire expertise in book lore if they are to invest wisely, avoid costly errors, understand catalogues and talk intelligently to dealers and fellow bookmen. They must pick up the basic jargon - the technical language of printing and binding and the terminology of catalogue descriptions of condition.

In order of importance books must be, first, complete, second, sound in condition and, third, properly and appropriately bound if they are to be deemed worthy of collecting. One missing page may devalue a book by more than 50% except in the case of the very rarest works which may still be valuable if stained, torn or incomplete.

Generally speaking true collectors will not give shelf-room to so-called 'reading copies'. These are incomplete, tatty, dirty or worn out books which are ugly to look at and have no other value than as a source of text. Occasionally such books are kept for cannibalisation so that two or more incomplete copies can be made up and rebound into one presentable, if phony book.

Before striking a deal to purchase a book it is the responsibility of the buyer to check its completeness, on the principle of 'caveat emptor' or 'let the buyer beware!' The checking procedure is called 'collation', leafing through every page to check its rightness, making sure that all plates, including the frontispiece, illustrations, engravings, half-titles and sometimes advertisement leaves are present and correct. The bibliography is the source of the first information for this. Comparison with another known complete copy is always helpful.

Books with missing plates are seriously devalued. Illustrations are often highly collectable and sought after by 'breakers' who loot illustrated books and frame the pictures for sale at inflated prices. The 1911 edition of Maeterlinck's 'The Life of the Bee' is valuable because of the 13 superb plates by Edward J. Detmold which it contains. Thomas Wildman's 'Management of Bees' (1st 1768 edition) may lose half its value if one of the three engraved plates is missing. Books bought at book auctions should be correctly described in the catalogue with their faults pointed out. Such books may be returned to the auctioneer and payment refunded because they are 'not as catalogue' if they prove to have undisclosed faults. Books offered for sale as part of a lot but not actually named and described - written down as 'others' - do not enjoy the same protection.

Reputable book dealers trading by post will treat customers with equal fairness. It is in their interest to show honesty and integrity with regular collectors. But a book picked off the shelves of a second-hand book shop should be checked with care If a dealer sells a valuable book to a personal caller there still remains a moral responsibility to disclose faults. A reputable trader will cancel the deal if his customer is unintentionally misled about the completeness of a book or is unsatisfied for any other reason.

Page numbers may not be a totally reliable guide to completeness when collating a book. Cotton's "My Bee Book" for instance has erratic and incorrect pagination, and this is a commonplace among early books. The 'gatherings' of older books are usually a better guide to completeness.

ii

To understand this we must realise that early books were printed on sheets of hand-made paper fabricated from rag. This paper was commonly 20 inches x 15 inches ("Crown") though there were nine other sizes ranging from 34" x 26" ("Atlas") to 17" x 13½" ("Foolscap"). Books are not printed one page at a time. Instead several pages were printed all together first on the front and then on the back of each large sheet of paper. Each face would have several blocks of print corresponding to 'sides' in the final book. If two blocks, or sides, were impressed on each face it would make folio pages, if four quarto pages, if eight octavos, then 16 mo right down to 128 mo.

The shorthand for these sizes, called the 'format' of the book, is 2o (or fol.) 4to, 8vo, 16mo, etc.

Once the large sheets, had been printed in blocks on both sides they could be folded as follows:

Once for "Folio" to give 4 sides.

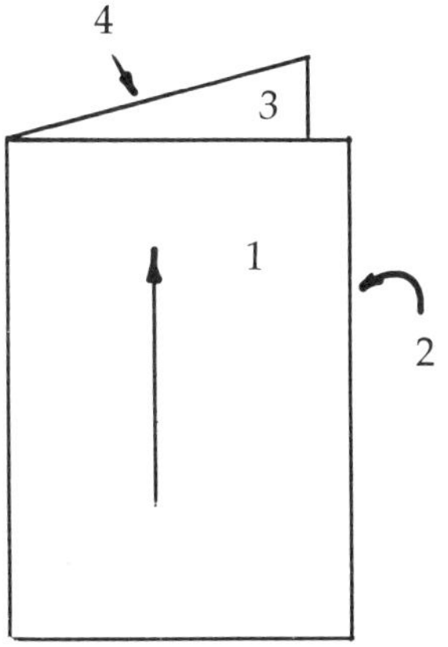

These would all be printed the same way up.

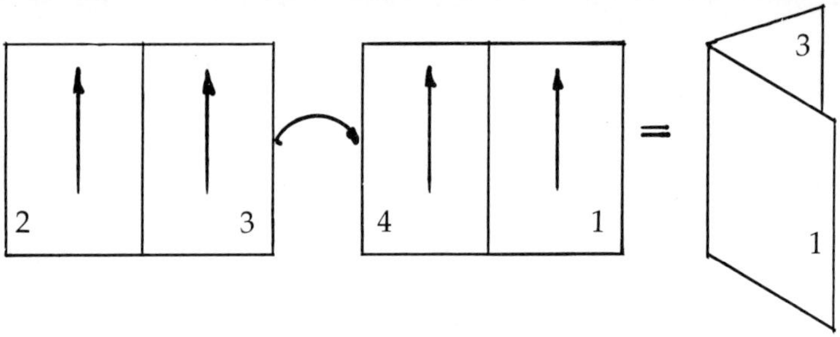

These are often big books, the sort that would be laid flat rather than upright on the bookshelf.

Examples are Hale and Swammerdam.

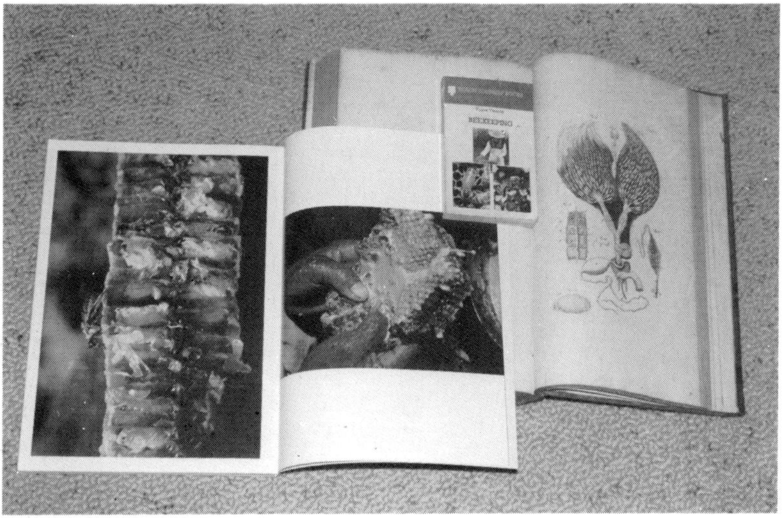

Folio books, ancient and modern, with a paperback to show their size.

The next size or format, is quarto. In this the crown size sheet is printed on each side with four blocks of print, with the print arranged in the direction shown by arrows.

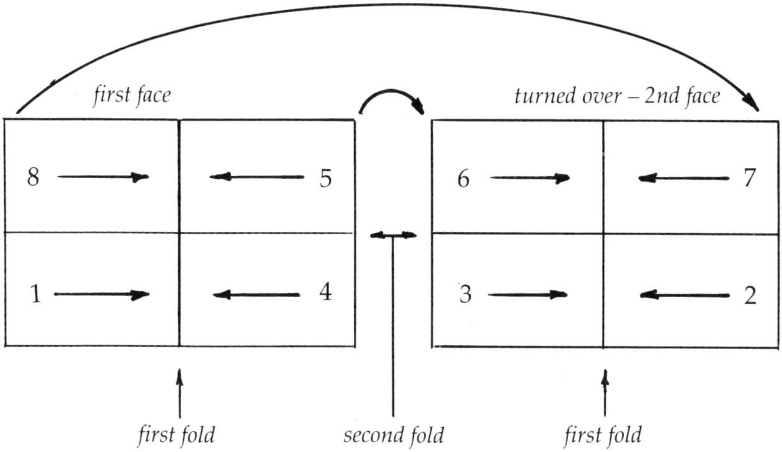

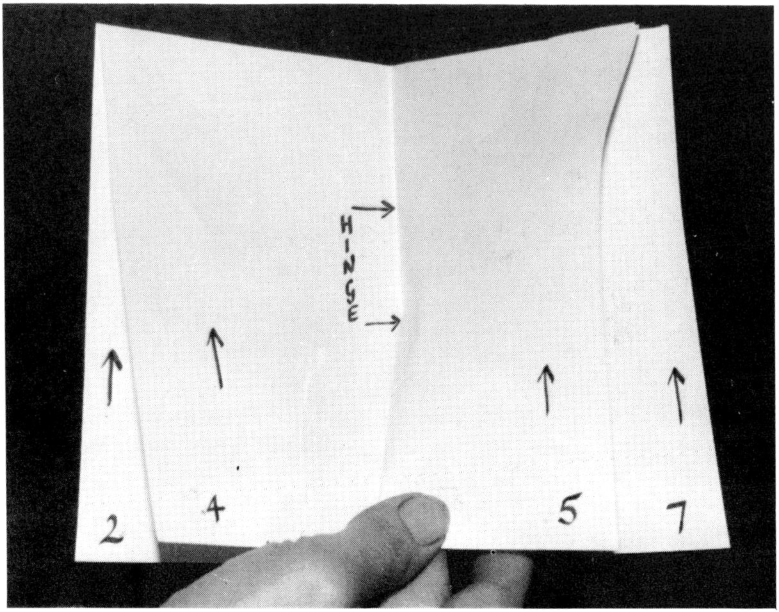

Then the paper can be folded once, then folded again so that the eight blocks of print make a little 4-leaf, 8 page booklet, printed on all 8 sides. If the rows of type are arranged as shown by the arrows no pages will be upside down.

The easiest way for the reader to grasp this is to make a model by folding up a piece of A4 paper.

Obviously if the original sheet were folded yet again then a booklet (or more properly a 'gathering') of 8 leaves (16 pages) would be produced requiring 8 blocks of print, properly arranged as to direction, on each face of the original sheet.

Yet another folding would yield 16mo or sextodecimo and so on.

As a variation the original paper could be folded differently to produce 12 mo and 24 mo. etc.

Many 'gatherings' or booklets would then be clutched together and each one stitched through the centre fold to make the spine. When all gatherings were in place then the top, bottom and fore edge of the collation could be guillotined through to cut off the free and folded edges to make the whole thing neat and sharp. This action produces a 'cut' book. If the edges are left 'uncut' then the folded parts of the edges have to be slit open with a paper knife to allow the reader open access to the pages. Such books are called 'unopened'. An uncut or 'untrimmed' book whether or not it has been 'opened' presents a rough and irregular set of edges. Books in such 'original' condition are highly prized by some collectors.

Printers provided a helpful guide to binders to ensure that, when the collation of gatherings was made ready for sewing each copy, every one was in the right order and the right way up. Each gathering had a 'signature' - usually an alphabetical letter, but sometimes a numeral - below the text on the first two or three leaves of each gathering. The signatures run from A to Z (usually without I or J and U or V) and if necessary start again Aa, Bb, Cc etc. and even Aaa, Bbb etc.

Another useful piece of information is the nature of watermarks in the paper, visible by holding a page up to the light. The three main marks in hand-made paper, up to 1861, are:

i) Chain lines - widely spaced
ii) Wire lines - narrow spaced
iii) The water-mark proper - a 'trade-mark' design.

A collector can check the correctness of a book by using this information. First he finds a position in the book where he can see the binder's thread in the gutter (fold) where the leaves meet. By counting back and forward to the next threads or to the signatures on each side he can assess how many leaves to a gathering - always an even number.

The direction of the chain lines then helps him confirm the format of the book. Because the original unfolded sheets are of variable size, format cannot be deduced from the dimensions of the book. If the chain lines happen to be horizontal and the watermark in the centre of the spine fold and there are four leaves or eight sides in each gathering, then it is a quarto book. If the chain lines are vertical, the watermarks at the head of the spine fold and each gathering has eight leaves, then it is an octavo. An ordinary novel is commonly in this format.

Providing the signatures are in place it is a relatively simple matter to check that:

a) all the gatherings are present and
b) each one is complete.

Any gathering with an odd number of leaves suggests a missing page - the most likely but not the only explanation.

'Catchwords' in older works are words printed at the bottom right-hand corner of a page, repeating the first word at the top of the following page. They were there to guide the binder when assembling a book. Now they are helpful aids to collation.

Signatures are much less open to error than page numbers because they were of vital importance to the binder. Page numbers were for the convenience of the reader alone and meant little to the binders or printers.

The beginnings and endings of books, often enough the most vulnerable to page loss, can also be more complicated to assess. The first signature may be B in an octavo book; 16 pages further on is signature C. The complications arise because the 'prelims' of a book may not make up a complete signature, or may be more than one signature, 'Prelims' are the introductory pages, preliminary to the main text. Often they fall into half a signature front, and half at the back (4 leaves each). End papers – the double leaves at the beginning and end of a book – do not nornally form part of a gathering, being cut and fastened in a separate operation by the binder.

In cases of doubt the collector should consult a bibliography, or failing that another perfect copy of the book.

iii

The Parts of a Book.

iv

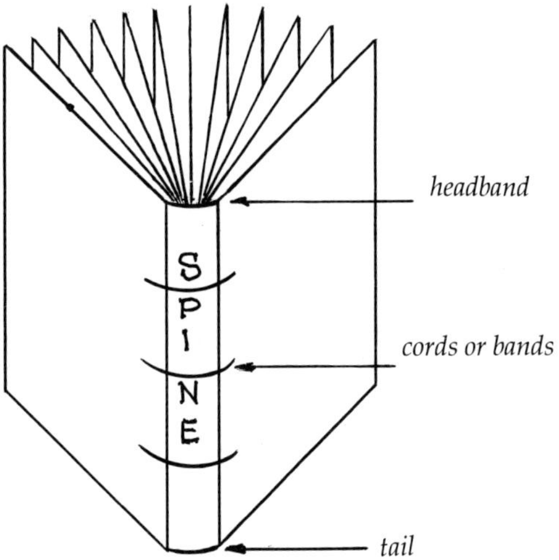

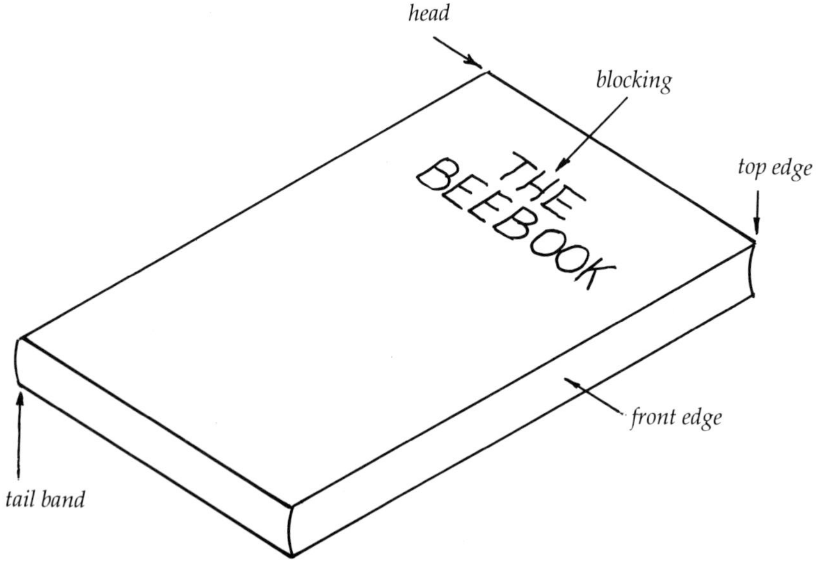

Glossary of Book Collectors' Words

A	*acknowledgements*	part of prelims. Recognition of help
	a.e.g.	all edges gilded.
	antique	a modern replica of an old style of binding
	association copy	copy of a book identified with someone or some event by inscriptions, signatures, marginal notes. etc.
	Atlas	large printer's sheets to make very large volumes.
B.	*band*	headband, tailband etc. see diagram and 'raised bands'.
	black letter	see 'gothic'
	boards	the outer covers of a book; the stiffening of the covers.
	bookplate	an engraved or printed label showing ownership, normally on front 'paste-down'.
	bookworm	avid reader or destructive larva
	browning	deterioration of paper through acidity of paper and age.
	buckram	strong linen or cotton, stiffened with size to cover boards
C.	*C.*	circa, around (of dates)
	calf	smooth leather tanned from calfskin. Fawn or dyed.
	cased	most cloth-bound books are cased. In bound books the covers are fitted by lacing the cords to the boards. With cased books, however, binding and printed parts are made separately, then united by machinery.
	catchword	first word of the following page, printed below the text. An aid for the binder assembling the book.
	cloth	treated calico for covers
	colophon	see 'printers imprint'
	cords	see diagram
	corrigenda	inserted slip of paper correcting errors found after printing
	cropped	margins cut back, possibly with loss of text, headline or numerals

	crown	common size of printing sheet (20" x 15") giving octavo 7½" x 5"
	cut down	smaller than it should be. May be an insert.
	cuts	woodcuts, illustrations printed from a piece of wood on which a design has been cut, or engraved.
D.	*dedication*	part of prelims. Author's tribute.
	de luxe	reckoned by the publishers to be specially good.
	disbound	has been bound, but no longer so.
	dog ears	creased corners of leaves.
	d.w. or D/W	dust wrapper - protective paper cover,
	dust jacket	sometimes decorative and valuable.
E.	*early printed books*	used of books before 1640
	edge	top, bottom and fore - see diagram
	edition	a complete set-up of type for printing. Any alteration of type produces a new edition. Major changes usually called 'New and Revised' edition.
	elephant	see 'Atlas'
	end papers	2 leaf sheet at the beginning and end (plain, blank, ornamental, marbled or printed on). One leaf of each sheet is pasted down to the inside of the covers (the 'paste-down')
	errata	note pasted in with prelims correcting errors in text
	ex-lib	with labels and stamps evident from a library.
F.	*facsimile*	inserted photocopy of missing page, a makeshift. Or a modern photographic reprint of an older work. Any copy.
	faded	original colour lost. Covers are sometimes called 'sunned' (bleached by sunlight).
	flyleaves	blank sheets fore and aft of a book which are, strictly speaking, not paste-down or free end papers. Sometimes misused for the latter. Extra free end papers.
	fly title	a second half-title, or a divisional title

		for distinct parts of a book.
	folio	a book format, made of any standard paper folded only once.
	foreword	part of prelims. Statement to the reader.
	format	the form of a book, resulting from the number of times the original paper was folded.
	foxed	with small brown-red stains, circular or irregular. Origin uncertain.
	front *frontispiece*	plate before title page
G.	*gathering*	a group of leaves resulting from the folding of a single printer's sheet.
	gothic	heavy early 'black letter' typeface.
H.	*half-bound*	spine and corners bound in one material and the sides in a different one.
	half-calf	leather back and triangular corners on boards.
	half-cloth	cloth, with paper boards
	half-title	abbreviated title page, preceding the printed title page proper
	headband	see diagram. Found at top of spine.
	hinge	where two leaves join, or the boards meet the spine. The joint.
I.	*impression*	the total of books of an edition printed on a single occasion. Also called a 'printing'
	imprimatur	an official licence to print (by church or state) on a prelim page.
	imprint	see title-page.
	incunabula	books printed before 1500 A.D.
	inscribed	autographed by the author
	issue	part of an edition, but incorporating minor changes, corrections etc. differing from an earlier issue of the edition.
L.	*laid down*	pasted on another piece of paper to strengthen a fragile item.
	laid paper	handmade paper which may show chain lines 25 mm apart, or

watermarks imitated by modern machinery

leaf — a sheet = 2 pages
list of contents — part of prelims, showing page
list of illustrations — numbers
loose — sewing, hinges and gatherings not tight, semi-detached from binding.

M. *morocco* — grained goatskin. Types include Levant, Niger, and crushed with the grain pressed flat.
mounted — see 'laid down'
M.S.(s) — manuscript(s)
mull — strips of linen or canvas, pasted to the spine just visible under paste-down. Scrim

N. *n.d.* — no date
nice — a book in good condition

O. *octavo* — format when the standard sheet is folded thrice. 8 leaves.
offset — stain caused by accidental transfer of ink from one page to the one opposite
opening — a pair of facing pages in an opened book

P. *page* — either side of a leaf
pagination — the numbering of the pages, sometimes irregular
parchment — sheepskin
paste-down — see 'endpapers'
pigskin — hardwearing leather, pigskin
pirated — an edition copied in contempt of copy-right. Unauthorised.
plate — illustration, separately printed
point — an oddity of a minor nature like an advertisement or misprint which identifies to which issue or edition a book belongs.
preface — part of prelims. Introductory statement
printer's imprint — sometimes on verso of title page - printers name and address. May be at end of the text (colophon)
provenance — history of the ownership of a copy of a book

Q.	*quarter-bound*	with the more decorative material on the spine only
	quarto	format when a standard sheet is folded twice
R.	*raised bands*	ridges over the horizontal binding cords onto which the gatherings of a book are sewn. They can be false.
	reading copy	too dilapidated to be displayed in a collection
	rebacked	spine recovered or restored
	recto	the first side of a leaf you come to in a made-up book. 'Verso' is the other side of the same leaf
	rubbed	used of the binding; strong but showing wear and tear.
S.	*section*	another word for 'gathering'
	shaved	see 'cropped'
	sheet	a leaf (or more if not yet folded)
	side	one face of a leaf
	signed	page bearing a 'signature' or in the usual sense, autographed by the author or illustrator.
	spine	see diagram. Back, where the pages are hinged.
	stained	self-explanatory!
	state	when titles, illustrations etc. change on reissue the original 'state' gives way to the second state, and so on.
T.	*tailband*	see diagram. Base of spine.
	tail	
	teg	top edge gilded
	title page	title, with publishers name and address at bottom, called his 'imprint' and the date.
	tipped in	page pasted in at the inner edge
	tissue	thin paper to protect plates
	top edge	see diagram
U.	*unbound*	never been bound, no covers
	uncut	not trimmed by the binder's guillotine
	unopened	folded pages still requiring to be slit open

V.	*vellum*	untanned calf, inner side
	verso	see 'recto'
	vignette -	small picture without borders
W.	*washed*	pages cleaned, to get rid of stains, and resized
	w.a.f.	with all faults. No redress after purchase. Non-returnable.
	watermark	logo of the papermaker, visible against the light.
	wire lines	narrowly spaced lines visible in laid paper

6.
Restoration and Repair

Like other antiques old books can be restored, so that many faults can be considered redeemable. Dirty pages can be washed, loose gatherings can be tightened, crumbling spines can be restored or the copy rebacked. Leather bindings can be repaired or renewed. Small tears can be patched and some stains eliminated. Skilled bookbinders and repairers can work wonders with a tired or badly shaken book with damaged covers. If the pages are all present most can be renovated and given a new lease of life. If a book has survived a hundred years it may be a duty and privilege to rejuvenate it for the twenty first century.

The buyer of such a book should try to purchase it at a price which, when added to the cost of repairs, does not exceed the value of a superior copy which might be bought already in good condition.

Missing pages can be replaced by facsimile photocopies from another volume. No buyer is deceived by this, though it may complete the book. By cannibalising another depleted volume it is possible to make good a valuable book. Though a deception this may be an excusable way of saving a precious artefact for posterity.

Stains may be removable. But if they are ineradicable, ugly and disfiguring they could render the book valueless. Books which have been soaked with water may not be totally worthless, especially if very old. But if the pages are stuck together or distorted, seriously wrinkled and water-stained, then the book is most likely only of curiosity value.

It is a fine judgment how worthwhile it is to have a book repaired. The collector must have regard to the potential value, the scarcity of the work and its importance in his own library.

7.
How book values are determined

The knowledgeable book collector must get to know the value of particular editions. Some works have a lengthy history of being 'in print' and some issues will be scarce and so more valuable. Numerous texts exist only in the one edition. They may never have sold well enough to warrant a second impression of the first edition, not to mention a second or subsequent edition.

An 'impression' is a reprint of a previous issue of the book without any changes to the typeface. It is exactly the same book reissued at a later date than the first printing of that edition. A further 'edition' occurs when either the typeface is changed or there are minor alterations to the text or both. Generally major alterations to the wording in the new edition, or variations in the illustrations merit the description "New and revised edition". Broadly speaking the earlier the edition the more valuable the work. But this is not an invariable rule, some later editions being better bound, scarcer or superior in illustrations or text than earlier ones. In works, where the value lies in modernity and being the last word in scientific knowledge the most recent version may be more valuable than the first imprint.

Ultimately, and probably sooner rather than later, the collector will be alone, facing the crucial decision – to pay the price or lose the book. That critical moment may last only the few seconds it takes at an auction to decide whether to wave the hand for one more bid, or shake the head and hear the precious volume being knocked down to another buyer. In a bookshop the time to make up one's mind may be more protracted and more gruelling, but the point of decision will still come.

Good judges say 'pay a good price for a good book you will be pleased to own'. Nothing is more irritating than to pass a scarce book for the sake of a few pounds and later realise that the chance of a lifetime has been missed, maybe never to recur.

The collector should try to judge a book on a system of values of his own devising. This should be an amalgam based on the date and edition of the book, its scarcity and condition and the reputation of its author with posterity. Values are determined by supply and demand. Charles Butler is famous so his book is 'wanted by every collector'. The more potential buyers there are the more the best customer who establishes the price will pay.

Some particular books have great breadth of subject matter. A work like the seventeenth century compendium 'A Way to Get Wealth' by Gervase Markham will appeal to aficionadoes of falconry, angling, cock-fighting, field sports, housewifery, orchards and gardening to mention only a few. Competition is much keener for such a work because of the multiplicity of potential customers. A similar book on one topic, even bees, might be cheaper. If it were a book of sermons it could be relatively valueless in the book trade – if not at the gates of paradise.

However encyclopaedic works, dictionaries and gentlemen's companions such as Nathaniel Bailey's 'Dictionarium Domesticum' of 1736 or 'The cyclopaedia' of Abraham Rees of 1805 in 39 volumes, which only treat of bees and all other subjects in a superficial fashion, will not create this same lusty enthusiasm to buy from many quarters at once.

The collector must remember that fashions change. But in the long run what counts are the factors already listed plus, in some instances, the reputation of the printer or the illustrator or any special quality in the binding.

Plates are of great significance in enhancing the value of a book. A first edition may be cheaper than a later one if it is not blessed with plates.

First editions always have greater value when there is a long time gap between them and subsequent editions. Later issues of constantly reprinted works such as those of Cowan and Digges are always relatively inexpensive.

The story of a well-known book, like T.W. Cowan's 'British Beekeepers Guide Book' may serve to illustrate the terms used to describe successive printings. The prices quoted are for a good copy in 1990.

This book was published from 1881 to 1924, and went through 25 editions in 43 years! The 1st edition of 1881 is now valued at about £30. The 1882 2nd edition is, strictly speaking, a second impression, or reprint of the 1st and might be worth £25. In 1883 25 more pages of text and 4 more pages of preliminaries were added, so it is now the "3rd revised and enlarged edition" worth £15/20. The 4th 1884 edition had just four more pages, and four more editions of similar length followed, the last two of which were each revised. (value £12). There had thus been 8 editions to 1886 - only 5 years.

The sequence of editions to the 18th in 1903 varies 5 times in the number of pages, fluctuating between 174 and 188. All editions to the 18th are published by Houlston. The 14th (1896) was revised thoroughly and has half tone engravings from photographs taken at W.B. Carr's apiary and 8 pages of evocative advertisements. With the 15th (1898) Cowan with 'distaste', allows his portrait to appear as a frontispiece. He writes proudly of "this half tone block on next page (sic), from a capital photo taken from life, of worker bees and queen on a frame of comb."

In 1907 the 19th edition was revised and enlarged by 46 pages and now published by Madgwick, Houlston and British Bee Journal, which Cowan edited. (£12) The next year saw the 20th "Coronation edition" - worth £14. By 1915, in the midst of the Great War, the

Quatuor Apum ordines.

Princeps.

Duces.

Plebs.

Inertes fuci.

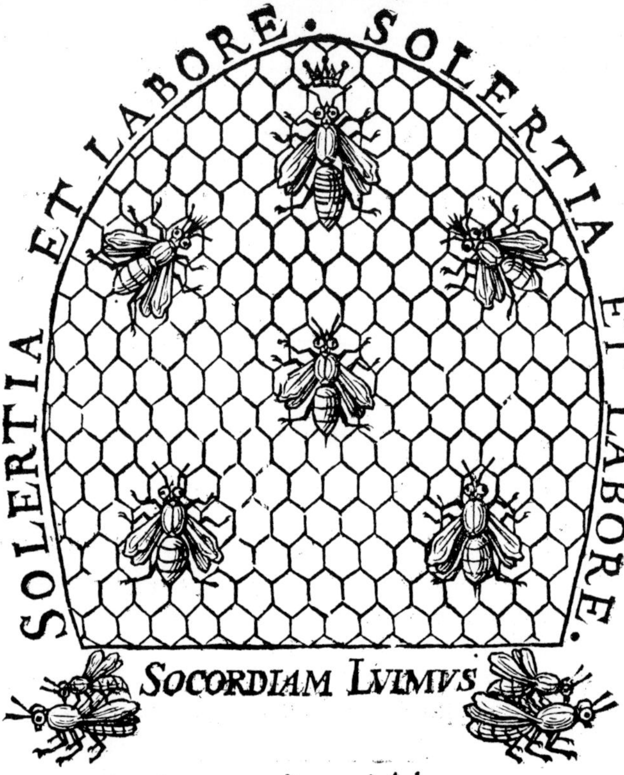

Miraris Arte conditas mirâ domos,
Opesque regales in his reconditas?
SOLERTIA ET LABORE *fiunt omnia.*

Deſe cur'ous buildings fraugt wit riceſt treaſure,
Not witout Caus,to ſoom doe Woonders ſeeme:
But dey, wit greater Caus, doſe Woonders Cauſes,
[Bæ's WIT and INDUSTRI] may Woonders deeme:
Deſe doe make doſe noe Woonders in reſpect:
For wat wil not INDUSTR'US WIT effect?

C.B.

Butler, engraved frontispiece to 3rd edition.

Houlston connection ceases (£8). The pagination remains constant at 226 after 1907 but the publishers change again for the 24th and final 25th edition of 1924 to Larby and the B.B.J. (£5). By this time 100,000 copies of the book had been issued over 43 years! It had also been translated into seven foreign languages, often in two or three editions.

At another extreme of value and rarity we can cite the most famous bee book, which is Rev. Charles Butler's 'Feminine monarchie' first printed in 1609 by Joseph Barnes and now worth about £500. The second edition, printed by John Haviland for Roger Jackson appeared 14 years later with eleven fewer leaves and a famous engraved frontispiece.

CAP. VII.

OF ÐE BE'S ENIMI'S.

ÐE good Bee', as oder good tings, hat many Enimi's; from wie ſee needet your help to defend her: namely, (1) de Mous, (2) de Wood-pecker, (3) de Sparrow, (4) de Tit-mous, (5) de Swallow, (6) de Hornet, (7) de Waſp, (8) de Mot, (9) de Snail, (10) de Emet, (11) de Spider, (12) de Toad, (13) de Frog, (14) de Bee', and (15) de Weder. — 1 *De Be's Enimi's ar many.*

Ðe Mous (weider hee bee of de field or of de hous) is a dangerous Enimi'. For if hee get into a Hiv'; hee tearet doun de Corns, mak's havok of de Hoonni, and ſo ſtarv's de Bee's. Soom enter by de door', or by ſoom open plac' in de skirts of de Hiv': ſoom gnaw a hol' torrow, in de top of de Hiv', wer' dey know de Hoonni lyet: ſoom keep' deir old' hom's, — 2 *1. De MOUS.*

Q 3

Butler's phonetics (3rd Edition 1634) Chapter VII 'Of the bee's enemies' showing marginal references.

Twenty five years after his first bee book appeared Butler had printed the 3rd edition this time by William Turner. This runs to 180 pages (wrongly numbered 182). It is a remarkable book since it exemplifies throughout Butler's own phonetic spelling system. He uses the old English letter 'thorn' (đ for th). He extends this to cut out h's: c for ch, w for wh, g for gh.

"Ðeir hearing and feeling ar very qik. If you touc đeir Hiv' but ligtly, or đe ftool', or đe ground neer' it; đey presently perceiving it, mak' a generall noys: alđowg Ariftole doubt weiđer đey hear, or not".

Then in 1673 R Richardson translated the book into Latin, published in London, and another Latin version appeared from Oxford 9 years later (1682).

By a curious twist 'W.S.' then retranslated the book back into English and it was published in London in 1704. G. Conyers who issued a catalogue of books on practical subjects re- published it using the same type the same year. So there are seven seventeenth century editions. The story is concluded by an 8th facsimile edition 300 years later (1969) and another in 1985 (Northern Bee Books).

The term 'facsimile' is used for a modern version of a famous antiquarian work now normally made by photo reproduction, but sometimes the text is reprinted afresh. Examples are Lawson's 'New Orchard and Garden' (1618) in 1927, Gerard's "Herball" (1597) in 1975 and Wildman (1768 ed) in 1970.

These modern reproductions are attractive items for collectors, but like repro furniture have no greater value than a similarly sized modern book. Indeed bearing in mind there are no rewards for the author and no designing costs such books should be less expensive to produce than a new text.

The date of a book and the edition may be obvious from the title page or its verso though the reader may need to know his roman numerals. The range of publishing dates will usually be from 1523 (Fitzherbert's 'Book of Husbandry') to the present day.

Seven letters need to be known:
M - 1000, L - 50, V - 5
D - 500 , X - 10. I or i - 1
C - 100

I and C and X can be repeated up to 4 times

e.g. VIII = 8

a letter after a higher letter means add on

a letter before a higher letter means take away.

e.g. IX = 10 - 1 = 9;

MDCLXXII = 1,000 + 500 + 100 + 50 + 10 + 10 + 1 + 1 = 1672

Most dates will be MDC (1600) + further letters.
Or MDCC (1700) + further letters.

e.g. 1608 = MDCVIII
1709 = MDCCIX

1633 = MDCXXXIII
1764 = MDCCLXIV

1697 = MDCXCVII
1784 = MDCCLXXXIV

Only occasionally do letters appear in sequences of 4

e.g. XIIII = 14

Sometimes the only evidence of the date of a book is to be found at the foot of a preface by the author.

Some books, especially when often reprinted, carry no date except that careful scrutiny of advertisements can reveal the year of issue. E.H. Taylor Ltd.'s 'Bees for Beginners' appears in grey, yellow, blue and red cloth. The advertisement at the end varies but dating is difficult. Sometimes inferences can be made from the text, from illustrations from the style of print or from 'points'. These are tiny errors which pinpoint particular issues. An error in titling workers and drones which should have an erratum slip identifies one printing of two of Taylor's yellow book (1923). The price on the cover rises - grey and yellow 2/6d, blue 3/-, red 3/6d. Inflation has some uses!

The oldest books can be identified by their black letter gothic print, and familiarity with design styles of printing and decorated initials and borders can soon enable a collector to assign a book to a general period. Bindings, to a lesser extent, help to date books, but they can be misleading. Eighteenth century books such as works by Thorley, Wildman and Bonner will often have a list of distinguished 'subscribers' or patrons who had pledged themselves to buy the book to ensure its publication. Nineteenth century books will be printed on machine made paper and mirroring the novels of the period, run to greater length and to more profuse illustrations as printing technology improved.

Leather bindings.

Larger folio works, stored flat.

This process continues into the twentieth century, though production standards dipped in times of austerity, most obviously during the economy years during and just after the 2nd World War. Post-war books are readily recognisable by their excellent design and the quality of photographic illustrations.

Bindings, and in particular attractive spines, are an important element of a book collection. They are the feature that catches the eye of the visitor and brings distinction to bookshelves. The collector will soon learn their characteristics. He will recognise older books bound in leather with raised bands and cloth bindings from about 1825. He will distinguish between 'bound' books where the gatherings are sown onto cords, the ends of which are attached to the boards, and the later 'cased' books. In these books the printed sections are put together in one operation, the bindings are made separately and then the two elements are united by machinery.

Until the end of the eighteenth century most books were issued in rough paper-covered boards. The buyer would take them to his own binder to be bound in his own personalised house style to match the rest of his library. Copies still in 'original boards' are highly prized. Because each customer decreed his own binding there is a total lack of consistency which one would have otherwise expected if publishers had done the binding themselves. However full-calf or half-calf bindings are always desirable whatever the date and whether contemporary with the sale of the book or the result of restoration.

Modern books are likely to be given the best valuation when they are complete with dust jackets in good condition.

Certain special nearly precise terms are used by book dealers in their descriptions in catalogues and lists to describe books they offer for sale. 'Mint' means indistinguishable from a new book, with dust wrapper perfect. 'Fine' means perfect in every respect, but just less pristine than 'mint'. It could have an inscription. 'Good' is a more flexible term. Such a book should be complete, without stain or marks or other obvious blemishes, but it will be recognisably 'second hand' to the eye and the touch. Dust jackets should be clean and well coloured, but may be slightly creased, worn or rubbed.

'Poor' means something considerably worse than 'good' so that 'average' is the only term we have for a 'quite good' book. A 'Poor' book may be warped, loose in its case, have missing prelims and be marked or stained. It may be called a 'reading copy'; and will only have value if it contains clean illustrations or if it is a very scarce title.

Values diminish with deteriorating condition. Assume that 'fine' is 90% of 'mint' value, 'very good' is 80%, 'good' 60%, 'fairly good' 45%, 'poor' 10%. Some of these percentages may err on the generous side. Shabby books sell cheaply unless they are exceptionally rare.

Acquisition and Dealing

The collector of bee books will soon find himself acquiring books from a variety of sources, some keenly competitive, some expensive, some of a kind that will find him hurrying home rejoicing, clutching some valuable work for which he has paid only a small sum.

Those looking for 10 pence bargains at jumble sales must be early in the queue when the doors are opened. Amateur bookfinders rush straight to the bookstall and snatch up every remotely collectable book. Similar tactics are needed at bazaars, fetes, W.I. sales, car boot sales, garage sales, and fund-raising book sales.

Speed is essential, and if a hoard of likely books is gathered up swiftly, without pausing for scrutiny, no great harm is done if most of them are valueless.

The few coins it takes to pay for them will be repaid with advantages if only one turns out to be a worth-while item. Bee books, poultry books, old cookery books, agricultural books, golf books, and so forth, picked up in this way will find ready buyers in the book trade.

One's chances of a stroke of good fortune at charity shops and on market stalls is small but hope springs eternal! The author found his first and best copy of Huber in a country antique shop in a pile on the shelves of a bookcase being offered for sale. The owners accepted £5 with alacrity. There is profit in knowledge. To this end every collector must know both his books, and their current prices. He may be an amateur, but as a specialist too he should be knowledgeable enough to compete with the general dealer at his own game, or at the very least, avoid being exploited by him. He should, for instance, be better placed to know the worth of particular editions of a work than the dealer who, at best, is only broadly aware of the likely value of that title.

One way to achieve this is to misuse a copy of 'British Bee Books' as a price record. The offered price in dealers' lists, auction house catalogue estimates (or better, actual prices realised) or any other market source can be entered regularly beside each listing, and dated to allow for uprating for inflation. A book is worth what someone will pay for it, but an average of several judgments will give a just idea of real value. The frequency of entry will be an indicator of scarcity. From this information the collector can deal with confidence whether he is buying or selling.

BAGSTER, Samuel, Jun. 222 1834
The management of bees: with a description of the "Ladies' Safety Hive". /London, Bagster & Pickering, 1834./xx, 244 p. illus. col. front./A B G N O P S . C M W
2nd ed./London, Saunders & Otley, 1838./xvi, 240 p. 2 leaves, illus. col. front./B G H O R S . C M W
3rd ed./London, Saunders & Otley, [1852]./xvi, 240 p. 2 leaves, illus. col. front./A B G H S . M W
Anr. 3rd ed./London, Griffin, 1865./xvi, 240 p./S . M

BEVAN, Edward, M.D. 201 1827
The honey-bee; its natural history, physiology, and management./London, Baldwin, Cradock & Joy, 1827./xxvi, 1 leaf, 404 p. illus./A B D G H N O P R S . M W
Anr. ed./London, Van Voorst, 1838./xxiv, 447 p. illus. front./A B D G H R S . M W
Anr. ed. rev. enl. and illus. by W. A. Munn./London, Van Voorst, 1870. xxiv, 1 leaf, 384 p. 18 leaves, pl. I–IX, col. pl. A–L, front./A B G S . M W
This ed. is numbered 3rd ed. on the spine though not on the title page.
U.S.A. ed. 1843./Johansson 61.
The 2nd ed. was dedicated to Queen Victoria.
Walker p. 7: '[Bevan] practised as [a] Doctor at Mortlake, and at Congleton, Cheshire. His health giving way, he retired to Bridstow, near Ross [(Hereford.)], where he began to study bees. His book . . . at once . . . brought him into correspondence with the foremost bee-keepers of his time. In 1849 he moved to Hereford, where he died . . . Ob. [in] 'The Cottage Gardener', Lond., Vol. XXIII. Feb. 28, 1866.'
Bevan also wrote an article on the length of life of the different members of the bee community in *Magazine of Zoology and Botany* (1): 57–62 (1837).
The frontispiece (Fig. 9) shows the author's bee-house.

Extracts from 'British Bee Books' annotated with prices (Bagster and Bevan).

The collector should be on the mailing list of the three main bee book dealers in Britain who deal by postal catalogues;

Northern Bee Books, Scout Bottom Farm, Mytholmroyd,
Hebden Bridge, West Yorkshire, HX7 5JS.

Bee Books New and Old, Tappingwall Farm, Stathe Road,
Burrowbridge, Bridgewater, Somerset. TA7 0RY.

B & K Books and Honeyfields, Riverside, Newport Street,
Hay-On-Wye, Hereford. HR3 5BG.

and also a number of those others who specialise in natural history, rural life, and self-sufficiency.

Wheldon & Wesley Ltd., Lytton Lodge, Codicote, Hitchin,
Herts. SG4 8TE.

Cottage Books, Gelsmoor, Coleorton, Leicestershire. LE6 4JF.

Veronica Mayhew, Trewana, Behoes Lane, Woodcote,
Nr. Reading. RG8 0PP.

Their lists are a good source of wanted books and of informed valuations. The fair collector must reciprocate the dealers' interest in him by making some purchases. The cost of compiling, printing and mailing catalogues is high. In the absence of a subscription fee the flow of free book lists will soon dry up if no business is done.

When recording the prices of books it is vital to note their condition which may be the cause of substantial variations in traders' book lists.

Specialists vary in their terms of trade, some requiring payment in advance with the order, others sending books on approval. The customer normally pays for postage and packing, especially on cheaper books and is responsible for returning them if they are not to his liking. It is more economical to review the specialists' stands at conventions and honey shows so saving mail costs - not to speak of negotiating small discounts.

General second-hand book dealers normally, but not always, house bee books under 'Natural History' or 'Insects' or 'Agriculture'. However some of the more collectable titles like Maeterlinck's 'The Children's Life of the Bee' (1920) or Cotton's translation of 'Buzz a Buzz' (1872) may well be found in the children's section. Some of the more excitingly chaotic shops arrange their books by size rather than subject! It can enliven a holiday to visit a cathedral city or a series of country towns and make a walking tour of the antiquarian shops. But one must not be too sanguine. Bee books are only rarely to be found, except for a few tedious titles that everybody already owns. If the dealer is kindly he may take your name and 'phone number and promise to call you when he lights on something interesting, or keep it aside for you. He may even keep his promise. But such is the popularity of the hunt you may find yourself just the last name on a list of similar potential customers. However the more people who know of your interest the more likely you are to receive offers. Cultivate your friendship with local bookmen. Your needs are their business.

Talk to everyone about book-collecting, especially the bee- keeping fraternity. Elderly beekeepers fade away to the land of milk and honey in the sky and their surviving spouse or heirs may wish to sell off their books to an honest buyer who makes a better offer than the local bookshop will afford.

A private collector should not be afraid of the competition of dealers. They must buy cheaply in order to turn a profit. He can outbid them and still secure good value.

Book fairs are worth visiting to find particular wanted titles, if not for real bargains. Each dealer present will know his stock and save you time searching his stand. Unfortunately some target bee books are also sought equally earnestly by other types of book enthusiast, for instance microscopists, agricultural historians, horticulturists, general entomologists and literary people. Luckily relatively few bee writers - Gay, Dryden, Pepys and Evelyn for instance - are high stylists who find a collectors market outside the "bee fancy".

Book auctions can be most rewarding. As in single dealing the private bidder has the edge over the dealer, with the possible exception of three circumstances. The dealer may have a known customer waiting for a particular title, in which case the dealer may bid up, even if he finally takes a smaller profit since it will be in his interest to look after his regular client. Sometimes a lot is made up as ' a shelf full' or a 'quantity' or even a 'tea chest full' of books. The total price may be quite high, even though each book is cheap in itself. The buyer may want only a few of the books in the lot and have many volumes to carry home and subsequently sell without loss. The problem is compounded if only part of the lot is bee books and the price may be inflated if one or more books on any topic other than bees are specially collectable. A particular volume among many may be lusted after by another buyer who will run up the bidding out of sight. Occasionally a quiet word with a successful bidder can tempt him to split such a lot at a premium price. Otherwise the successful bidder must sell off the unwanted books at the next auction or elsewhere. The third difficult circumstance is when the lot contains one or more books with valuable plates which tempts 'breakers' to bid high.

The bidder must not forget that there is usually a buyers premium to pay, with V.A.T. on that premium on top of the hammer price. If he resells at auction he will pay a further seller's premium on the item resold. If you buy a book for £100 you spend £111.50 (£10 premium + £1.50 V.A.T.). If you are forced to resell at the same hammer price of £100 you actually collect at best £88.50 (10% premium + V.A.T. = £11.50) so the 'misdeal' may cost £23 as a forfeit price.

The Property of a Gentleman

584 BEACH (S.A.) The Apples of New York, 2 vol., *hole in spine of vol. 1, 1905*—Hedrick (U.P.) The Plums of New York, *1911*; The Cherries of New York, *1915*; The Peaches of New York, *1917*; The Pears of New York, *1921*; The Small Fruits of New York, *1925, plates, the majority coloured, some leaves spotted*—Hedrick (U.P., *editor*) Sturtevant's Notes on Edible Plants, *portrait, 1919, original cloth, slightly rubbed, a few marks, Albany, 8vo and 4to* (8) £180-220

585 BEVAN (EDWARD) The Honey-Bee; its Natural History, Physiology and Management, *first edition, additional title with wood-engraved vignette, illustrations, a few spots, original boards, printed paper label, short tear at head of spine, slightly rubbed at edges, but otherwise a very good copy, top edge trimmed, others uncut, from the sale of books belonging to Richard Payne Knight and Thomas Andrew Knight at Downton Castle, November 22, 1951,* [*British Bee Books 201*], *8vo, 1827*

90

Edward Bevan (1770-1860) was a physician and eminent apiarian. This treatise established his reputation in the latter field. £120-150

Extract from a Sotheby's catalogue.

Nevertheless composite lots may contain several valuable works, enough to justify a few brave bids.

It is important, even vital, to view books in advance of the sale. Sometimes this can be done in the morning of an afternoon or late morning sale, thus saving a second expensive journey to the salerooms. Though the auctioneer takes responsibility for the collation of named books and for describing faults it is for the buyer to assess value. This is especially true of multiple lots where the auctioneer's estimate may be deliberately imprecise. The buyer must calculate his maximum reasonable bid, pricing each book separately and totalling their value. The wise buyer notes his top price and bids no more than once beyond it. If he leaves a commission bid with the auctioneer's clerk, a porter or a friend that will be the limit. They will

Auction sale of illuminated manuscripts at Sotheby's, New Bond Street. Coronation of Henry and Matilda. Sold for £8,140,000. (Picture courtesy of Sotheby's).

not bid again. Commission slips are available for bidders to use at viewing times. The bidder should discipline himself against being "carried away", fighting it out beyond his prepared judgment. He stays cool while bidding, though he is living for thirty seconds at a high point of climactic excitement!

Notable auction houses are Sotheby's in New Bond St. or Billingshurst, Christies, Phillips, Bloomsbury Book Auctions and Bonhams.

They will all mail catalogues by subscription which can be expensive, but are helpful since they carry estimates and are informative artefacts in their own right. Subscribers may also be sent slips showing actual bid prices after the sale. Though visiting these rooms may be costly and time-comsuming it is a pleasurable adventure. Being present to bid is better than leaving a commission. One feels in greater control, and fully aware of the circumstances in which the sale is made. The bidder should get into a position where he can be seen by the auctioneer and bid with a clear gesture. Many auction houses now issue identifying 'paddles' with a number to be shown when the hammer falls. These are picked up at the door in exchange for your name and address. Strangers to an auction should also be prepared to establish their credit before the sale either by a written reference or personal support by someone known and trusted.

No collector should feel overwhelmed by the fame and reputation

751 Nutt (T.) Humanity to Honey Bees . . . revised, enlarged, and edited by the Rev. Thomas Clark, *wood-engraved plates and illustrations, cloth, spine faded, Wisbeech, 1839* — Huber (M.P.) The Natural History of Ants, *2 engraved plates, one coloured, original boards, uncut, worn, 1820* — Ormerod (E.L.) British Social Wasps, *15 plates, several coloured, original cloth, 1868* — Fabre (J.H.) Bramble-Bees, *original cloth, 1915*; The Mason-Bees . . . translated by Alexander Teixeira de Mattos, *presentation copy from the translator, original cloth, spine discoloured, New York, 1914; and an odd volume, 8vo and 12mo* (6) £100-120

140

752 Purchas (Samuel) A Theatre of Politicall Flying-Insects wherein especially . . . the Bee is Discovered and Described, part 1 only (of 2), *lacks c1-2, Ee2, and second part, slightly spotted, contemporary calf, neatly rebacked, 4to, 1657* £100-150

240

753 Rusden (Moses) A Further Discovery of Bees, Treating of the Nature, Government, Generation & Preservation of the Bee, *first edition, 4 engraved plates, 3 folding, contemporary calf, rubbed, rebacked, corners repaired, 12mo, 1679* £150-180

300

754 Walker (H.J.O.) Descriptive Catalogue of a Library of Bee-Books collected and offered for sale by Lt.-Col. H.J.O. Walker, *original cloth-backed boards, small 4to, 1929* £20-30

60

755 Warder (J.) The True Amazons, or the Monarchy of Bees, *engraved frontispiece, lacks first ?blank leaf, 1765:* Wildman (D.) A Complete Guide for the Management of Bees, *2 folding engraved plates, title and several catchwords shaved, 1792:* Thorley (J.) An Enquiry into the Nature, Order, and Government of Bees, *engraved plate, plate and several fore-edge margins shaved, B3 and H4 torn with slight loss, lacks last ?blank leaf, 1774*, 3 works in 1 vol., *nineteenth-century half calf, rubbed, rebacked, 12mo* £100-120

140

756 Warder (J.) The True Amazons: or the Monarchy of Bees, *second edition, engraved portrait, spotted, contemporary panelled calf, slightly rubbed, rebacked [British Bee Books 74], 8vo, 1713* £120-150

100

757 Wildman (T.) A Treatise on the Culture of Peach Trees, to which is added a Treatise on the Management of Bees, *folding engraved plate, contemporary calf, lightly rubbed, 12mo, London and Dublin, 1768* £100-150

170

758 Worlidge (J.) Vinetum Britannicum, or a Treatise of Cider . . . to which is added, a Discourse teaching the best way of Improving Bees, 2 parts in 1, *second edition, 3 engraved plates, 2 other illustrations in text, contemporary manuscript annotations on endpapers, slightly spotted, contemporary calf, worn, 8vo, 1678* £250-300

350

The Property of the late Rt. Rev. M.A. Hodson, sometime Bishop of Hereford

747 Butler (C.) The Feminine Monarchie, or the History of Bees, *second edition, lacks frontispiece (supplied loose in photocopy), slightly stained, old vellum-backed boards, uncut, small 4to, 1623* £80-120

£230

748 Butler (C.) The Feminine Monarchie, or the History of Bees, *third edition, lacks frontispiece, title defective, a few headlines shaved, some staining, calf-backed boards, Oxford, 1634* £80-120

200

749 Keys (John) The Antient Bee-Master's Farewell, *first edition, 2 engraved plates, half-title, contemporary speckled calf, lightly rubbed [British Bee Books 154], 8vo, 1796* £150-200

180

750 Lawson (William) A New Orchard and Garden . . . with the Country-Housewife's Garden . . . as also, the Husbandry of Bees, 2 parts in 1, *woodcut vignette on title, woodcut plans and other illustrations in text, somewhat stained, half calf, 4to, 1653* £100-120

130

1984

90 1645 **Bees: Huber (Francis) New Observations on the Natural History of Bees,** *"2nd edn.", folding engd. plate, ink lines in margin, sl. soiled, uncut, cuttings pasted on prelims, orig. boards,* Edinburgh 1808;
85 Keys (John) A Treatise on the Breeding and Management of Bees, *2 engd. plates, uncut, sl. stains, orig. boards, spine worn,* 1814;
85 Gelieu (Jonas de) The Bee Preserver, *uncut, rather loose, orig. boards,* 1829;
60 Bevan (Edward) The Honey Bee in Natural History Physiology, *frontispiece, engd. vignette on title, illus. in text, sl. loose, orig. cloth,* 1838;
60 Wildman (Daniel) A Complete Guide for the Management of Bees, *2 folding engd. plates, browned,* 1801, *bound with* A Short
25 and Simple Letter to Cottagers from a Conservative Bee-Keeper, *lacks back wrap,* Oxford 1838, *later cloth, worn* (5) *8vo* £80-120

405 ? Estimated value 15th Ed Hammer price £320

Extracts from Sotheby's catalogues.

£440 — bargain!

272 THORLEY (J.) Melissologia [*greek*], or, the Female Monarchy, *5 engraved plates (frontispiece a little torn), a few leaves somewhat spotted and stained, contemporary calf, somewhat worn, 1744* — Wildman (T.) A Treatise on the Management of Bees, *second edition, 3 engraved folding plates, a few leaves loose, 1770* — Nutt (T.) Humanity to Honey-Bees, *second edition, illustrations, somewhat spotted, original cloth, slightly worn, 1834* — Jardine (*Sir* W.) Bees, British & Foreign, *Naturalists Library edition, portrait, engraved title and 29 (of 30) plates, some coloured, some slight spotting, original cloth, slightly rubbed,* [*c.1840*]; *and 4 others on bees, 8vo and 12mo* (8) £250-300

200 120 65 40

Bevan 1838, 40, Nutt 6th 1845, 40, Keys 1796, 175, Jardine 1859, 40

Extract from a Sotheby's catalogue.

of well-known auction houses. Every honest buyer is welcome in the world of trade. Prices may be high, but they will be the prices that match demand in the keenest market place of all.

There are dozens more less famous salerooms all over the country such as Dominic Winter, at Swindon which will be equally worthy of attention. It is likely that provincial salerooms will be less frequented by the more prestigious dealers. Such houses may also be willing to catalogue collectable books which are expected to fetch less than £50 a lot.

These days bidding by phone is often possible. The buyer may use it himself to save a lengthy journey or be prepared for bids against him from this source.

When buying at auction get comfortably established in your place before the lot comes up. Calculate the auctioneer will sell up to 120 lots an hour, so do not be late and concentrate on bidding till the moment of truth has passed.

The book trade is short of stock so few items will be completely overlooked by the dealers. Bargains are to be found just the same.

You can find out prices made at auctions by consulting BAR - 'Book Auction Records'. This is published annually and is usually to be found in public libraries. One drawback is that the condition of the book sold at the quoted price is not revealed. Also you can never be sure whether a book is so rare and valuable that it has never appeared at an auction, or so common and cheap that no copy has been sold as a single item.

Collectors soon find that their shelves become congested. Circumstances conspire to furnish them with numerous copies of books which they do not need. These will be finds and 'pick ups' reckoned bargains, copies of books which have been superseded by newly acquired better copies, and the residue of mixed lots bought at auction. These books represent substantial locked-up capital. While it is true that such spare copies are growing in value at the pace of inflation they could be converted by trading into better books which equally well would retain their real value while enhancing the quality and quantity of different books in the library. The collector should sell as well as buy.

He should list his surplus books, price them at a just sum, photocopy his list and advertise it in 'Beecraft' or some similar journal. Alternatively he can offer, them at modest prices, to specialist or general dealers.

If he wishes he could sell the lot through a book auction house, making up his books into well-balanced saleable groups. Unless the books are antiquarian this will best be done through a provincial saleroom. It still pays him to advertise the view- days and date and place of the sale in a bee journal to catch the interest of other collectors who might otherwise be unaware of the opportunity offered.

Even antiquarian books acceptable to Sotheby's, and given international publicity in their glamorous catalogues, could stand a little cheap home-spun publicity.

9.
The Care of Books

The way to preserve books in perfect condition would be to store them in the dark, in dry, dust-free,temperature-constant conditions at perfect humidity:

Temperature: 55 - 68F (13 - 18C)

Relative humidity: 55 - 65%

6 air changes per hour.

But such a collection would be of little use for reference, for decoration of for the solace and joy of its owner.

Books should be readily available for reading and displayed to give satisfaction and pride to their owner and lend graciousness to his home. They deserve open shelves in a handsome bookcase. They should be arranged so that the tails of their spines are aligned with the shelf edge and so that they support each other upright without being tightly jammed together. If they are too tight the headbands will be damaged when the books are picked out. They are best kept in a cool room where the temperature does not fluctuate much from month to month. They should be in a shaded position, for sunlight bleaches and rots them. They will need dusting from time to time with a feather duster or soft cloth, especially on the top edges. They should be taken out for random inspection sufficiently often to detect any damp spots in walls behind them which might otherwise be hidden and overlooked.

Books should not be overheated or kept in musty rooms in damp cellars, or any room which freezes. In smoky or polluted atmospheres closed bookcases are preferable to open shelves, but glass-fronted cases exaggerate any overheating from direct sunlight. Wooden shelves, especially unpainted ones, assist in humidity control, but guard against woodworm which is a plunderer of books. There should be a six-inch cavity behind the books when shelved and the bottom shelf should have a six inch gap beneath it. This helps to protect books from floods, pets or both. Avoid fireside alcoves beside real fires and open up windows and doors to air the room whenever weather permits. House fires and firemen's hoses have sealed the fate of thousands of rare books, so that not only fire insurance but also efficient smoke- detectors should be placed in book rooms. Automatic sprinklers however may be an extra hazard rather than a help. Mould follows damp and is more damaging. Valuable soaked books should be kept wet and cool until given specialist restoration by an expert. If they dry closed the pages may stick together beyond redemption.

Leather books tend to dry out and lose their flexibility. This can be remedied by careful use of British Library dressing, (Messrs. Boots C1590), which consists of Anhydrous lanolin 175g, Cedarwood oil 25ml, Beeswax 12g, Hexane (or petroleum ether, BP 60 - 80) 270ml; or a simpler mixture of 40% neatsfoot oil and 60% anhydrous lanolin rubbed in very sparingly on cotton wool, then polished when dry. Potassium lactate cleans and preserves leather but will not prevent decomposition once it has started.

Books can be cleaned up in several simple ways. A good soft pencil rubber, kept clean, will remove pencil marks and improve covers when stained and marked. Brush well first, then rub in one direction only - spine to edges. Test carefully before erasing marks on coloured paper. Some ink stains will respond to this treatment, preferably with a stick-type pencil eraser, but be cautious and always support covers carefully when rubbing opened books. Ink may respond well to ultra fine sandpaper if it is used with great delicacy. The page should be held up to the light every few strokes to avoid over-thinning. Do not remove celebrated signatures or marginal notes made by such people. An 'association copy' is to be preferred to a plain one. The author's collection is improved by several copies with 'E Tickner Edwardes' inscribed on the endpaper. Chemical ink eradicators like potassium permanganate or proprietary brands should be tested out before use on comparable paper. They may discolour paper. Ball pen fades, but often pits paper deeply. Marking ink is irredeemable, as are 'highlighter' stains. Deep rubber stamp marks may have to be covered with a book plate! Light sanding may help if the ink has not penetrated too deeply into the fibres. Rust may be sanded or touched with hydrogen peroxide on a glass rod.

Transparent adhesive tape should not be used to mend tears except on the reverse of dust jackets. It can be removed with hexane or cleaning fluid. The latter will remove white wine stains, and red wine stains can be washed with white wine. Use blotting paper and waxed paper to protect neighbouring pages when treating any page with fluids. For mould stains one can try peroxide, lemon juice and brief exposure to sunlight, or alcohol with thymol in it.

Loose pieces of leather or cloth or paper can be fixed with home made starch or flour paste. Do not use commercial adhesives like PVA which may mend up well, but in an irreversible way, storing up future trouble. Copydex or other latex adhesives are to be avoided. A book with loose boards or in need of rebacking should be tied up with cotton tape or neatly tucked into a card wrapper so that it is protected until rebound by a binder in a manner appropriate to its period. Ancient books that have fallen into such a frail state that rebinding could do more harm than good can best be preserved by boxing them in suitable containers that resemble a book in shape with a hinged lid. Original rare bindings should be preserved for posterity.

Rebinding books with proper materials is expensive. £50 to £100 would be a likely figure, but bigger books and tougher challenges might double or treble those prices. When costing books that need rebinding, or have been recently rebound these factors cannot be ignored. A useful comparison would be with the relative values of a restored and unrestored vintage motor-car.

Books suffer most, like bees and beehives, from careless manipulation by their handlers. They should be eased out of bookshelves by their backs, not by tugging at the headband. They should be held in the flat of the hand, or laid on a table with a support for the opened cover. All barbarisms like scribbled notes, ink marks, tea cup rings, use as a flower press or door stop or prop or kitchen weight and dog-eared corners are to be eschewed. Significant damage can be done by dropping books on their edges or cracking the spine to hold the volume open.

Babies and toddlers have functions and artistic enthusiasms highly inimical to the preservation of good books. Keep them at bay. The author's copy of Hill's 'The Profitable Arte of Gardening' (7th edition, 1586) is embellished on page 56 with this legend:

"Margaret Jubb is my name and with this pen I write the same if my pen had bene better I would have mended every letter" marginally to be preferred to 'Get out you dog' in another volume of similar vintage!

10.
The Story of Bee Writing

i Pre-Caxton

Before 1500 AD all bee books are manuscripts, written by hand, not printed. 'British Bee Books' identifies 12 manuscripts which make reference to bees. Collectors are unlikely to acquire them except in facsimile.

ii Early printed books to 1500

Gutenburg began printing in Germany in 1455 and Caxton set up the first English press in 1477. Printed books from 1455 to 1500 are known as 'incunabula' - (Latin: swaddling clothes) the cradle of books. These are generally 'black letter' books, so called because they are printed in heavy Gothic type. Strictly speaking there are no bee books of the incunabula period, though some of the earliest works are indeed in Gothic lettering.

iii Early printed bee books to 1600

Fifteen books are listed, in the 16th century. The first of these is John Fitzherbert's 'Book of husbandry' (1523)* which ran to 12 editions to 1598. It had only two pages of bee matter. The first book which has a separately written treatise specifically on bees is Thomas Hill's 'The proffitable arte of gardening', the third tyme set fourth, of 1568. We have to wait until 1593 for a book totally on the subject. This is Edmund Southerne's 'Treatise concerning the right use and ordering of bees' which is written from practical experience rather than being derived from classical and other authorities.* It contains a famous yarn about a parson and tythe bees retold by W.C. Cotton in

16 ROBERT D. STEEDMAN, BOOKSELLER.

Gardening. Hill (Thos.) The Profitable Arte of Gardening, now the third time sett forth : to which is added much necessary matter, and a number of secretes, with the Phisicke helpes belonging to eache Hearbe, and that easily prepared. To this is annexed two proper treatises, the one entituled, The marueilous gouernement propertie and benefite of Bees, with the rare secretes of the hony and waxe. And the other, The yeerely coniectures meete for Husbandmen to know. Englished by Thomas Hyll, Londoner : Whereunto is newly added a treatise of the Arte of grassing and planting of trees. Sm. 4to, printed in Black Letter, *with woodcuts*, (some writing appears on the title and the margin of one or two pages), newly bound in full calf, *Lond., Printed by Robert Walde-graue*, 1586. £9 9s.

The march of inflation a) old catalogue £9. 9. 0. b) Sotheby's estimate £200 c) hammer price £450.

* *In this instance and other familiar references to publication the date given is for the first published edition in English.*

* *"Better late than never" as the extended title declares!*

1675 **Hartlib (Samuel) His Legacy of Husbandry,** *3rd edition, woodcut decorations, contemporary half-calf, worn, one cover detached* small 4to 1655 £120–180 170

1676 **Hill (Thomas, editor) The Profitable Arte of Gardening, now the thirde time set forth,** *woodcut illustrations, mostly black letter, a few 16th or 17th Century, marginal annotations, pieces missing from one margin not affecting text, old half-calf, broken in two, covers detached, possibly lacking one leaf of the Table of "A Profitable Instruction of the Perfite Ordering of Bees", sold not subject to return*
small 4to Henrie Bynneman 1574
£150–200 450

Auction catalogue entry for Hill. Hammer price over double the estimate.

'My Bee Book'.

The remaining twelve early books are herbals (e.g. Gerard's 'The Herball', 1597), or books of husbandry with bee material (e.g. Conrad Heresbach's 'Foure bookes of husbandrie, 1577), natural histories, gardening books, the first known translation of Virgil's 'Fourth Georgic' or poetical or metaphorical pieces.

In short beekeeping was not a common subject of the earliest printing presses, which may be some relief to the earnest collector, since books of this period are likely to attract bids of £500 or more at auctions.

iv Bee Books to 1699

'British Bee Books' lists the books of the 17th century under the general banner 'The beginnings of bee science'

Although a slavish adherence to the erroneous opinions of classical authorities still characterises the writings of many authors, there gradually emerges a number of honest works based on practice and enquiry. At the very dawn of the seventeenth century came the first English version of the 'Maison Rustique' (1600). This was translated by Richard Surflet having originally been written in Latin by Estienne in 1554 and then revised and translated into French by Jean Liebault.

But the major work, sought by all collectors, and outstanding for *the firſt Treatiſe.* 23

¶ How the dead Bees may be reſtored to life againe. Cap xix.

The képer of bées ought to foreſée and take héede, that the Bées peryſh not through ouer great heate, or ouer mighty cold. If at any time by a ſodaine ſhowre in the ſéeking for foode, Bées happen to be beaten downe, or nipped wyth a ſodaine colde (which ſeldome ſo commeth to paſſe that the Honny bées are ſo deceyued,) that harmed with the droppes, they lye groue-lyng and flatte on the earth, as dead in a manner, then gather the Bées togyther, putting them into ſome veſſel for the nonce, which after ſet in a warm chamber or Parloure, & couer warm ymbers, beyng ſomewhat more than hote, on the Bées, whiche gently ſhake with the aſhes, but in ſuche ſorte that you touche them not wyth your hande. And ſetting the Bées in the ſunne, and neare to their hiues, they will after recouer, and flie again into their cotages.

Gothic, or black letter print. Thomas Hill 1574.

591 Estienne (Charles) and Jean Liebault. Maison Rustique, or the Countrie Farme. . .translated into English by Richard Surfleet, *first edition in English, woodcut device on title, woodcuts in text, some full-page, complete with first blank, somewhat dampstained in places, one or two small holes (e.g. M1), a few leaves slightly wormed in outer margin (e.g. T4), modern panelled calf in antique style, [STC 10547], 4to, Edm. Bollifant for Bonham Norton, 1600* £300-400

594 [Hale (Thomas)] A Compleat Body of Husbandry. . .to which is annexed, the whole Management of the Orchard, the Brewhouse, and the Dairy, *first edition, engraved frontispiece, 12 plates, contemporary ownership inscription on title, calf-backed boards, folio, 1756* £100-150

Catalogue entries: Estienne and Liebault and Hale.

Butler's four part song, half printed upside down.

When so encreased is this prudent Nation,
That their own limits cannot them suffice;
To seek new Cities, for new habitation,
They send abroad their num'rous Colonies:
Antiope the prim' Princ' gon,

Orithya soon,
Of hir Qeen-mother, making mon',
Begs the like boon:
That with hir train hir fortun' shee may seek;
And this shee sings in metur's moornfull sweet.

BASSUS

A S of all stat's the monarchie is best; So of all Monarchi's that Fe-mi-nin',
They woork in common for the common-weal: Their labour's restles to maintain their stat':

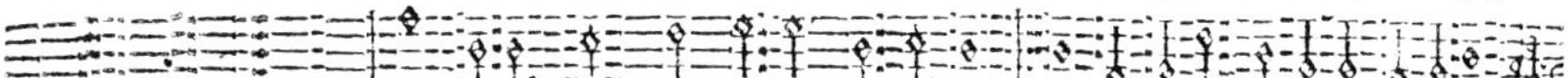

Of famous Amazons excels the rest, That on this earthy spher' hav' ever bin.
Their Hexa-gonia no Be-za-leel, for cur'ous Art may pas or imi-tate.

Whos' little harts in weaker sex (so great in field) No power of the might'st Mal's can mak' to yeeld:
On' Sov'raign, & but on', commands this people loyall, The great Marpess' with plenty blest of issu' roy-all:

They living ay, most sober and most chast, Their pain-got goods in pleasur' scorn to wast.
An-ti-o-pe, and Ori-thy-ja fair, With o-ther Princes, hir In-fan-tas ar.

I

TENOR

A S of all stat's the Monarchi' is best; So of all Monarchi's that Fe- mi- nin',
They woork in common for the common weal: Their labour's restles to maintain their stat':

Of famous Amazons excels the rest, That on this earthy Spher' hav' ever bin,
Their Hexa- gonia no Beza- leel, for cur'ous Art, may pas or imitat',

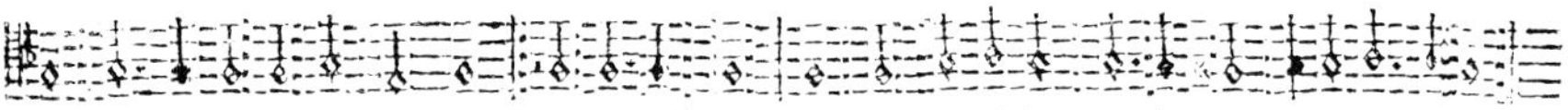

Whos' little harts in weaker sex (so great in field) No power of the might'est Mal's Can mak' to yeeld:
On' Sov'raign, & but on', commands this people loyall, The great Marpess' with plenty blest of issu' roy- all:

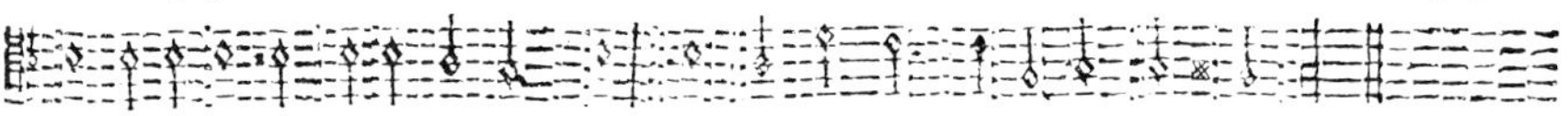

They living ay, most sober and most chast, The'r pain-got goods in pleasur' scorn to wast.
An- ti- o- pe, and O- ri-thy- ja fair, With o- ther Princes, hir In- fan- tas ar.

To whos' grav' accents if her Princ'ly Grac'
Vouchsafe, with Trine Aspect, reply to make,
To sweetest Treble tuning sweeter Base;
This moornfull suit a joyfull ende dooth take.
And then, when fit time they espy,

Soon thousands strong,
This Armie royall gallantly
Dooth march along.
Hark, hark, mee thinks, I hear in Notes of choice,
This fairest Ladies sweetest moornfull voice,

its own or any period is Rev. Charles Butler's 'The Feminine Monarchie' in three early editions, the first appearing in 1609. It is a magnificently comprehensive and indexed work which may be read today for pleasure and profit. The third edition of 1634 illustrates not only Butler's skill as a beekeeper but also his splendidly lucid style and his wide-ranging genius. He was parson, musicologist, apiarian, writer and spelling reformer. He invented his own phonetic orthography and contrived to put 'The Feminin Monarchi' through the press spelt throughout in his own unorthodox fashion. The book is also famous for its four-part song printed so that four singers could all stand round an opened book. The two who stood at the head-band end could read their parts because they were printed upside-down!

All fifty-three seventeenth century books are highly collectable and if in fair or good condition will be worth over £300. Famous names to note are Gervase Markham ('Cheape and good husbandry' 1614) Lawson ('A new orchard and garden' 1618), Levett 'The ordering of bees' (1634), Thomas Mouffet who was an authority on spiders, the author of 'The theater of insects' (1634) and probably the father of 'little Miss Muffet', Richard Remnant ' A discourse or historie of bees' (1637). Samuel Hartlib who wrote 'The reformed common wealth' in 1655 (£750 in 1989) and Samuel Purchas' A theatre of politicall flying-insects' (1657).

The historically minded will recall that we are discussing a hundred years which takes in Shakespeare and Milton, the Civil War and the Restoration. It was a time of enormous upheaval and political and religious change. Yet behind the conflicts lay the quiet peace of bees and beekeepers, farms and gardens and the men who wrote about them.

In mid-century Evelyn and Pepys the famous diarists are both included in the canon. Forty pages of Evelyn's 'Elysium Britannicum' until recently only in manuscript (reprinted 1966) is on bees and Pepys is interested in transparent hives, as were Evelyn and Charles II. Robert Hooke's work 'Micrographia' (1665) contained the first representation of a part of a bee - the sting - as revealed by a microscope. Samuel Pepys bought a copy on 20th January, 1665, the year of publication and wrote in his diary:

'To my bookseller's and then took home Hook's Book of Microscopy, a most excellent piece, and of which I am very proud'.

Primitive microscopes had been used earlier. Cesi's famous three bees were drawn as early as 1625 and we find the engraving used as a frontispiece to Thorley's 'Female Monarchy' (1744) but altered by his son in later editions for use as a trade card. The degree of magnification used was obviously small, but sufficient as an aid to the artist.

There are a number of books subsequently published on microscopy with bee matter the most notable including

ΜΕΛΙΣΣΗΛΟΓΙΑ.
OR, THE
Female Monarchy.
Being an ENQUIRY into the
Nature, Order, *and* Government
OF
BEES,
Those Admirable, Instructive, and Useful
INSECTS.
With a New, Easy, and Effectual METHOD to preserve them, not only in COLONIES, but common HIVES, from that cruel DEATH, to which their Ignorant, Injurious, and most Ingrateful OWNERS so commonly condemn them.
A SECRET unknown to past AGES, and now Published for the Benefit of MANKIND.
Written upon Forty Years
OBSERVATION *and* EXPERIENCE.
By the REVEREND
Mr. *JOHN THORLEY*, of OXON.
Illustrated with COPPER-PLATES.
Celsus ap. Origen cont. Cels. L. 4. p. 217.
LONDON:
Printed for the AUTHOR; and Sold by N. THORLEY, at the *Lock* and *Key* facing the *Mansion-House*; and J. DAVIDSON, at the *Angel* in the *Poultry*, *Cheapside*.
M DCC XLIV.

Thorley 1st Edition with Cesi's bees.

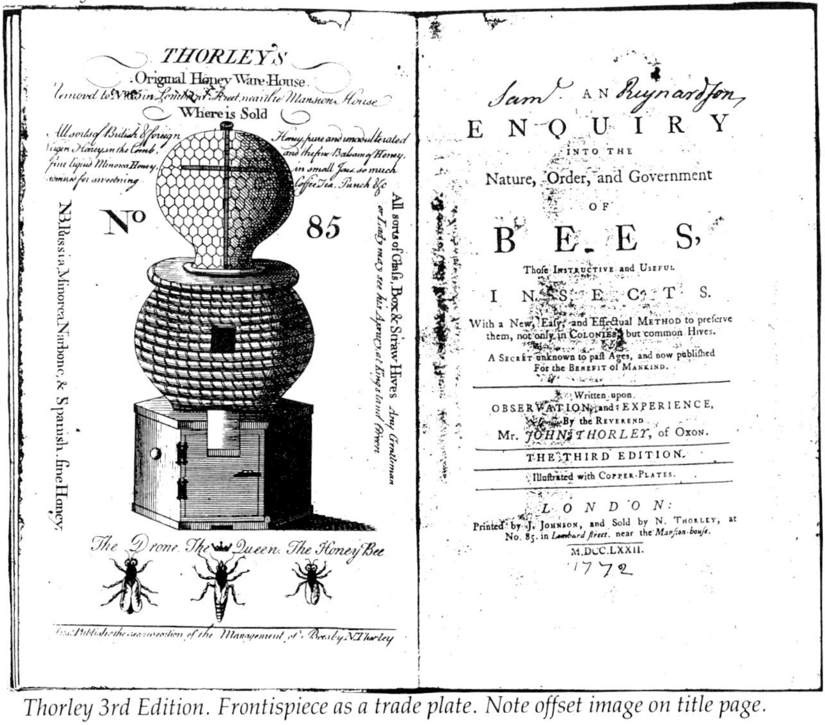

Saml. Reynardson
AN
ENQUIRY
INTO THE
Nature, Order, and Government
OF
BEES,
Those INSTRUCTIVE and USEFUL
INSECTS.
With a New, Easy, and Effectual METHOD to preserve them, not only in COLONIES, but common Hives.
A SECRET unknown to past Ages, and now published For the BENEFIT of MANKIND.
Written upon
OBSERVATION and EXPERIENCE,
By the REVEREND
Mr. *JOHN THORLEY*, of OXON.
THE THIRD EDITION.
Illustrated with COPPER-PLATES.
LONDON:
Printed by J. JOHNSON, and Sold by N. THORLEY, at No. 85. in *Lombard street*, near the *Mansion-house*.
M.DCC.LXXII.
1772

Thorley 3rd Edition. Frontispiece as a trade plate. Note offset image on title page.

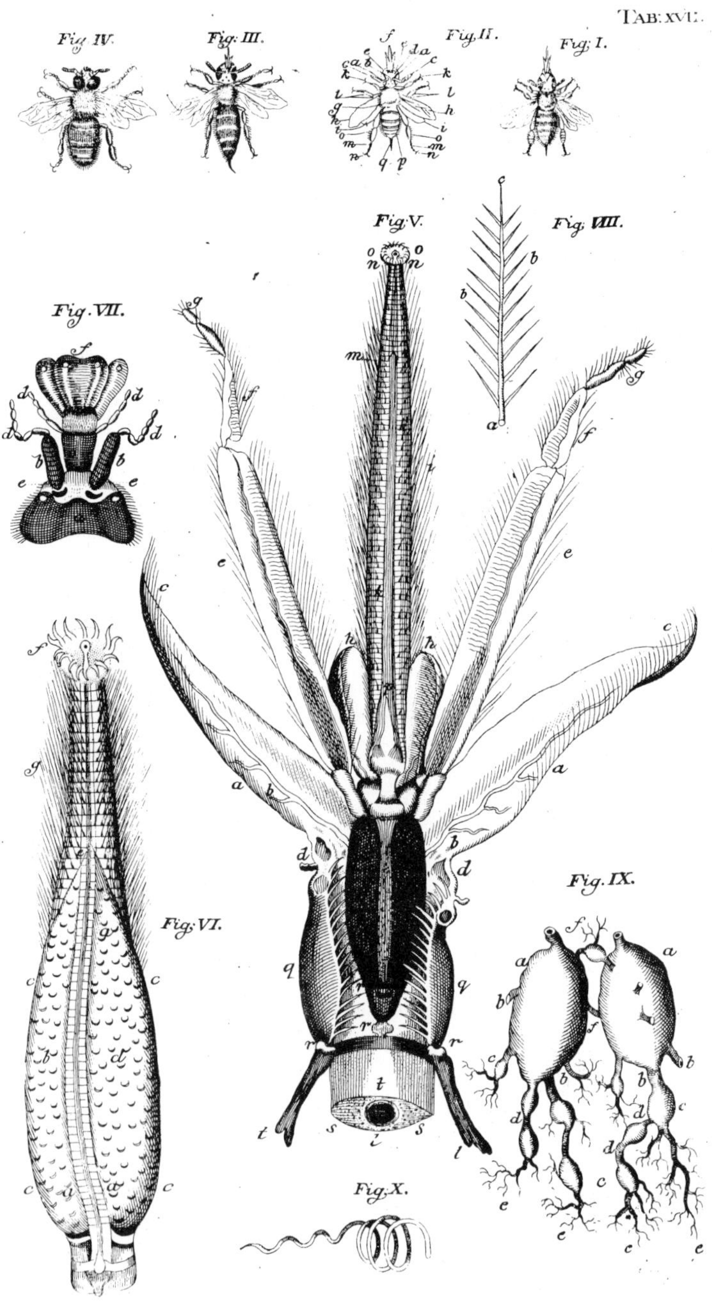

Plate s showing mouthparts and eye from Swammerdams 'Book of Nature' (reduced).

TAB. X

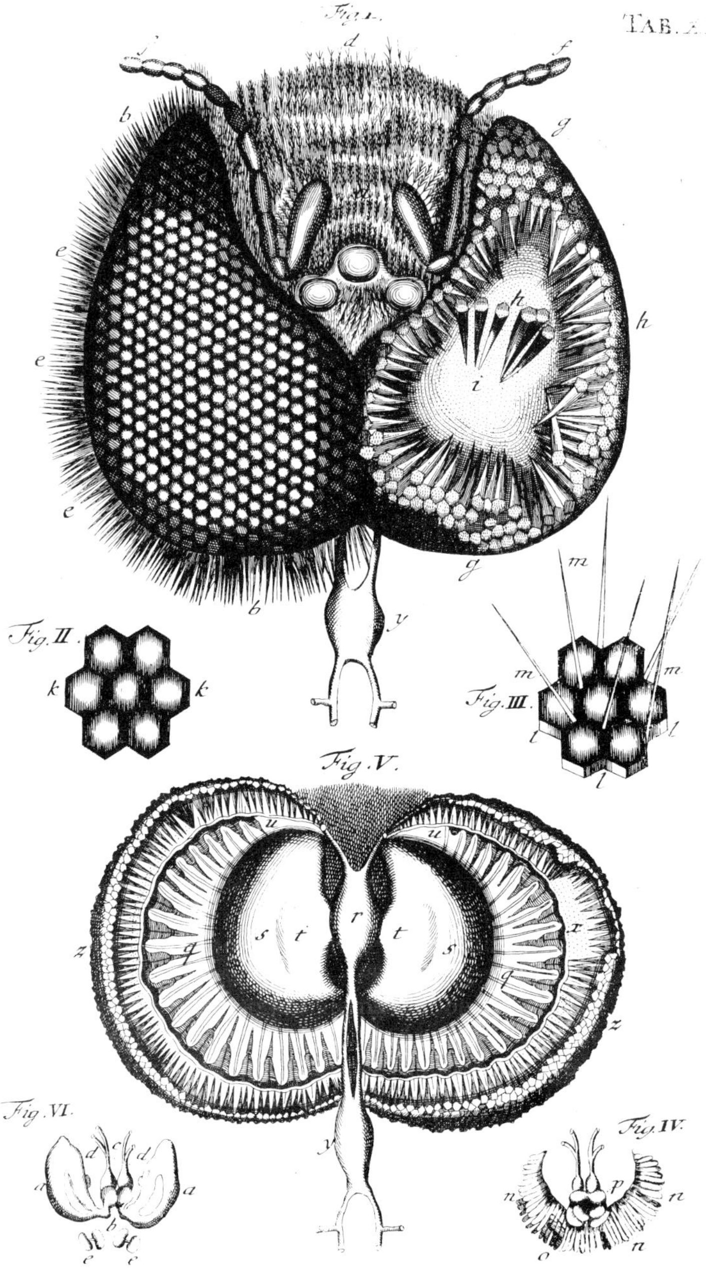

reproductions of the Dutchman, Antony van Leewenhoeck's drawings of the sting and mouth parts issued as 'Philosophical transactions of the Royal Society' in 1673 and reprinted in 'British Bee Books'. Henry Power (1663) had written of the subject and in the early 1670's another Dutchman, John Swammerdam was concluding five year's intensive study of bees under the microscope. However it was not until the next century that the story unfolded further. Then came Henry Baker and his 'The microscope made easy' (1742 and four subsequent editions), George Adams and 'Micrographia illustrata' (1746 showing the sting and tongue) and to crown it all the first translation "done into English" by Thomas Floyd in 1758 of Swammerdam's 'The book of nature' with notes added by Dr. John Hill. This folio work contains nine plates with magnificent anatomical illustrations of bee-parts under the microscope which bear ready comparison with modern studies.

Reverting to the seventeenth century after this microscopical digression, we encounter the books of the restoration period. "The closet of Sir Kenelm Digby" of 1669 is the first full account of the making of metheglin, meathe and hydromel and other alcoholic wines. Many works on mead are to follow down the years, and these volumes would make an interesting sub-collection in themselves. Not surprisingly tippling was not a matter for publication during puritan times!

General agricultural works continue to make reference to bees, one of the most celebrated being that of John Worlidge ('Systema agriculturae', 1669) which has a beautiful frontispiece which includes an apiary with fifteen skeps. Worlidge's 'Apiarium' of 1676 was more directly concerned with bees, and two other of his works 'Systema horticulturae' (1677) and Vinetum Britannicum (1678) include references to beekeeping and metheglin.

John Gedde in 1675 produced 'A new discovery of an excellent method of bee-houses' which promoted his own patented beehive, a design not favoured by Worlidge. Moses Rusden (1679) with a similar hive and a similar title 'A further discovery of bees' gave his account of beekeeping methods and of the use of transparent boxes. Evelyn secured for him the appointment of 'Beemaster to King Charles II'.

Other desirable books from the early 1680's are William Mather's 'The young man's companion' (1681) which has bee and mead sections, and was an interesting study guide written by a schoolmaster. Sir George Wheler's 'A journey into Greece' has a notable passage on beekeeping on Mt. Hymettus, still famous for its honey. For the first time he draws attention to their practice of using bars on skeps to start combs which were then moveable. Wildman used bars over 80 years later but omitted to point out the advantages of moveable combs. The Greek practice was a big step towards the development of moveable frame hives, but it took over 150 years for

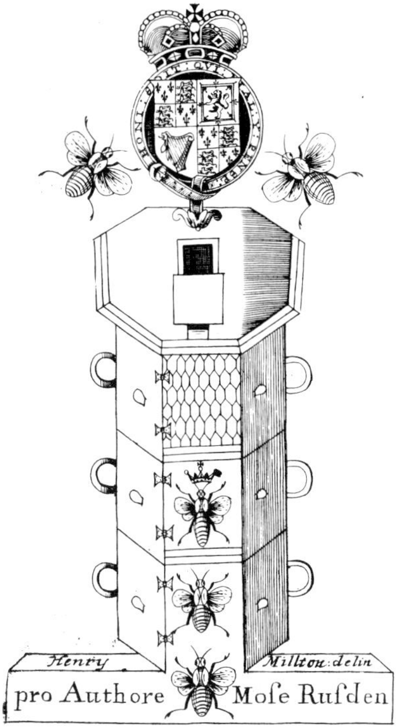

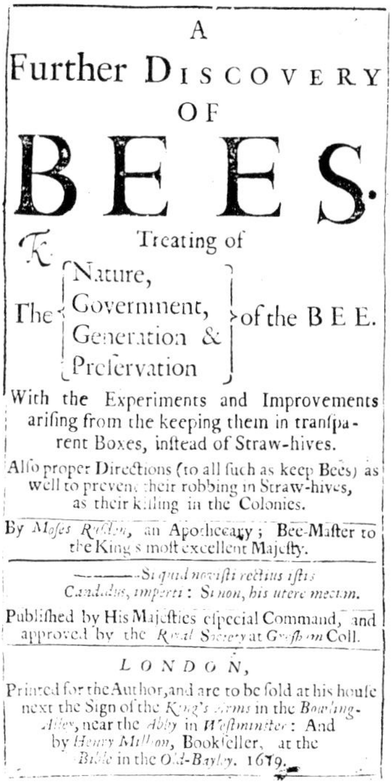
A
Further DISCOVERY
OF
BEES.
Treating of
The Nature, Government, Generation & Prefervation of the BEE.
With the Experiments and Improvements arifing from the keeping them in tranfparent Boxes, inftead of Straw-hives.
Alfo proper Directions (to all fuch as keep Bees) as well to prevent their robbing in Straw-hives, as their killing in the Colonies.
By Mofes Rufden, an Apothecary; Bee-Mafter to the King's moft excellent Majefty.
Si quid novifti rectius iftis Candidus, imperti: Si non, his utere mecum.
Publifhed by His Majefties efpecial Command, and approved by the Royal Society at Grefham Coll.
LONDON,
Printed for the Author, and are to be fold at his houfe next the Sign of the King's Arms in the Bowling-Alley, near the Abby in Weftminfter: And by Henry Million, Bookfeller, at the Bible in the Old-Bayly. 1679.

Moses Rusden's book – by Royal Appointment! 1679

the penny to drop!

Dyden's versification of Virgil into English at the end of the seventeenth century is notable not only for Virgil's bee lore but also for three engravings on bee subjects, two of which were by Wenceslaus Hollar . Five further editions followed the 1697 issue.

v. Books of the Eighteenth Century

The period 1700-1800 has the usual list of important early agricultural and horticultural works with references to bees. Evidently the legacy of the tradition of the Anglo-Saxon'bee-ceorl' (churl) was a common acceptance of beekeeping as a normal part of the rural economy. It is easy to forget that sugar was a rarity until the 1600's when the West Indian sugar plantations began, so that honey was the only sweetener that ordinary folk could afford to pleasure their palates. Sugar was still more expensive than honey right up to 1800.

Early works include:

Houghton, John - Husbandry and trade - 1702
Moore, Sir James - England's interest - 1703

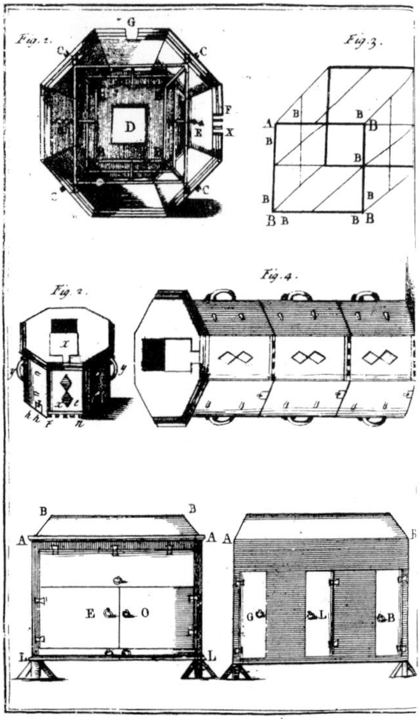

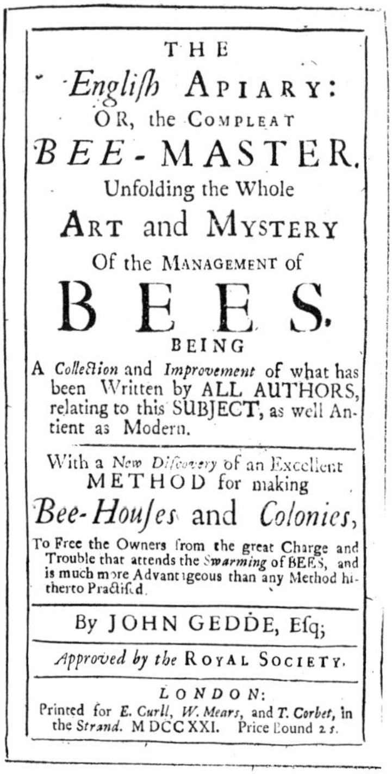
THE

English APIARY:

OR, the COMPLEAT

BEE-MASTER.

Unfolding the Whole

ART and MYSTERY

Of the MANAGEMENT of

BEES.

BEING

A *Collection* and *Improvement* of what has been Written by ALL AUTHORS, relating to this SUBJECT, as well Antient as Modern.

With a *New Discovery* of an Excellent METHOD for making

Bee-Houses and *Colonies*,

To Free the Owners from the great Charge and Trouble that attends the *Swarming* of BEES, and is much more Advantageous than any Method hitherto Practis'd.

By JOHN GEDDE, Esq;

Approved by the ROYAL SOCIETY.

LONDON:

Printed for *E. Curll*, *W. Mears*, and *T. Corbet*, in the *Strand*. MDCCXXI. Price Bound 2 s.

John Gedde: The English Apiary, together with a reprint of 'A new discovery' of 1675 (1721).

Dictionarium (Rusticum) - 1704
Mortimer, John - The whole art of Husbandry - 1707
Stevenson,Rev Henry - The young gardener's director - 1716
(with seven further editions)
Bradley, Richard - The country gentleman... - 1718
- A general treatise of husbandry - 1721
- The country housewife - 1727
and his translation of
Chomel - Dictionaire oeconnomique - 1725
Laurence Rev.John - A new system of agriculture - 1726
Columella - Of husbandry - 1745 (trans.Curtius)
Ellis, William - Modern husbandman - 1731
Agriculture improved - 1745
Hale, Thomas - A compleat body of husbandry - 1756
Lisle, Edward - Observations in husbandry - 1757
Harte, Walter - Essays on husbandry - 1764
A Society of Gentlemen-The complete farmer - 1766
Cooke, George - The compleat English farmer - 1772
Goldsmith, Oliver - A history of the earth and -

animated nature - 1774
and many subsequent editions.
Ringsted, Josiah - The farmer - 1775
Thompson Wm. - The new gardener's calendar - 1779
Cooke, Samuel - The complete English gardener - 1780
Monk, John - An agricultural dictionary - 1794

All these titles among others carry references to or sections on bees and beekeeping often derived or copied from the writings of English or foreign apiarists.

Other eighteenth century works with incidental bee material include entomological and zoological books, literary and religious pieces, dictionaries and natural histories. Examples of such books include:

Moses Harris - An exposition of English insects - 1776
James Barbut - The genera insectorium of Linnaeus-1781
Thomas Boreman - Description of 300 animals - 1730
John Gay - Fables (and 350 later editions!) - 1738
William Derham - Physico-theology - 1713
Bernard de Mandeville- The fable of the bees - 1714
Dr.John Arbuthnot - The congress of bees - 1751
Mythogelastic Cosmo (pseud.) - A political satire
by John Hall Stevenson - Makarony fables - 1768
Jacques Vaniere trans. by Murphy - The bees - a poem - 1799
Nathaniel Bailey - Dictionarium domesticum - 1736
Early editions of the Encyclopoedia Britannica - 1768
Gilbert White - Natural History of Selbourne - 1789
William Smellie - The philosophy of natural history - 1790
Robert Heron - Elegant extracts of natural history-1792

Aside from the foregoing diverse titles there are about a score of highly collectable 'dedicated' bee books of the eighteenth century all attracting high prices when in good condition. £200 would be a likely price for the works of beemasters who made their contribution to progress in apiculture.

In 1712 Joseph Warder, Physician of Croydon, had his book 'The true amazons' put on sale at the Buck and Sun in Fleet Street. Walker in his 1929 catalogue refers to a contemporary inscription on a page of the 5th edition which asserts: 'The author of this tract has been a Presbyterian, a soldier, a Quack and everything. But for Bees .... no man in ye world did probably understand them better'.

Collectors may note that while some inscriptions, book plates and marginal notes may devalue a book, others, especially the signatures of notable owners can place a premium on the copy! In this same edition Warder, in an added letter, defends himself from the charge, by Charles Nourse in a 1721 reprint of Gedde's 1675 book, that

THE TRUE

AMAZONS:

OR,

The MONARCHY of

BEES.

Being a New Diſcovery and Improvement of thoſe Wonderful *Creatures.*

Wherein is Experimentally Demonſtrated,

I. *That they are all govern'd by a* QUEEN.
II *The Amazing Beauty and Dignity of her Perſon.*
III. *Her extraordinary Authority and Power.*
IV. *Their Exceeding Loyalty and unparallel'd Love to their* QUEEN.
V. *Their Sex, Male and Female.*
VI. *The Manner of their Breeding.*
VII. *Their Wars.*
VIII. *Their Enemies, with Directions plain and eaſy how to manage them, both in Straw-Hives and Tranſparent Boxes; ſo that with laying out but Four or Five Pounds, in Three or Four Years, if the Summers are kind, you may get Thirty or Forty Pounds* per Annum.

Alſo how to make the *Engliſh* WINE or MEAD, equal if not ſuperior to the beſt of other WINES.

By JOSEPH WARDER of *Croydon*, PHYSICIAN.

The Third Edition with Additions.

Sic vos non vobis mellificatis Apes. Virg.

LONDON, Printed for JOHN PEMBERTON, at the *Buck* and *Sun* over-againſt St. *Dunſtan*'s Church in *Fleet-ſtreet*, and WILLIAM TAYLOR at the *Ship* in *Pater-noſter-row.* 1716.

'The True Amazons' by Joseph Warder. 3rd edition of 1716.

To the Book-Sellers. vii

Mr *Gouge*, Mr. *Hill*, my Ld. *Bacon*, and the Reverend Mr. *Purchas*; which laſt has juſtly obſerved, That *The Knowledge of* BEES, *was never truly communicated to the World, by any, but by* Engliſhmen; * and his OPINION is farther confirmed by the Accuracy of this Performance, wherein all that is *Uſeful* in the abovementioned Writers, is *carefully preſerv'd*; and their *frequent Excurſions*

* *See his* Theatre *of* Political *Flying-Inſects, in* Quarto, *Pag.* 102.

Charles Nourse's letter to the Booksellers in the 1721 edition of Gedde's 'The English Apiary'.

Warder "largely transcribed from others"

Nourse, interestingly enough, in his address to the booksellers, writes that he has carefully collated Gedde's work with that of the "antients-Columella, Varro, Aristotle, Pliny and Virgil, and among the English moderns – Southern, Levit, Butler, Remnant, Hartlib, Lawson, Gouge, Hill, Lord Bacon and Mr Purchas which last (Rev. Purchase) has justly said that 'The Knowledge of BEES was never truly communicated to the World, by any, but by Englishmen'".

This remarkably chauvinist viewpoint could not in truth be sustained much longer. By 1721 when Nourse wrote his note Swammerdam's work on bees was done but still unpublished, Maraldi, the Italian, had already published 'Observations sur les abeilles' (1712) ['Englished' in 1742] and Reaumur's work would appear in 1744 in a version by Gilles Bazin. European scientists were indeed at work on forwarding 'Knowledge of bees' in ways which were unmatched by the favourite sons of the Royal Society of England.

Joseph Warder gave 'plain and easy directions on managing bees in straw hives and transparent boxes' and promised good profits for beekeepers. His work was popular and ran to nine editions to 1765.

In 1733, by order of the Dublin Society, came the first Irish bee book

'Instructions for managing bees.' This would be followed down the years by several worthy Irish works. The most successful would be 'The Irish Bee Guide' of Rev Digges which ran to a new title 'The practical bee guide' and 16 editions through the first half of the twentieth century!

In 1744, the same year as Bazin's version of Reaumur, appeared the next great bee book. This was the Rev. John Thorley's 'Melisselogia' or 'The female monarchy' with four interesting plates in the first edition and a copy of Cesi's three bees for a frontispiece. The three authentic later editions (1765, '72 and '74) have only two plates. Pirated editions appeared in 1745 and 1760. Good copies of the 1st edition are now worth £200-250. Thorley advocated, and claimed to be the originator of the use of the puffball as a narcotic to stupefy the bees but save their lives when taking away the honey or uniting colonies. In this he was presumptuous since Gerard had mentioned it in his 'Herball'.

'The Practical bee-master' of 1747 by Robert Maxwell was characterized by Walker as 'an important book by a well-educated but retrograde bee master'. His was an early Scottish contribution to bee letters to be followed like the Irish by many fine works in later years. James Petrie's 'Scots' Apiary' of 1769 was such a work. Welsh books are fewer. 'British Bee Books' lists only three.

Dr. John Anderson writing in 1938 in 'Bees,Honey and Beekeeping' (S.B.K.A.) records how John Hunter in 1879 in his 'Manual of beekeeping' writes that "The cottagers of Scotland far exceed the English in the ability they display in Bee-Keeping". Anderson notes the names of John Gedde of Fife, Maxwell, James Bonner, Howatson, William Dunbar, Pettigrew the skeppist, Kerr who made the Stewarton hive, named after his Ayrshire village, McPhedran the "Renfrewshire Beekeeper", Thomson an early wax foundation moulder, Macdonald, Cheyne the surgeon who researched bee disease with Cheshire and Anderson and Rennie who with Bruce White discovered acarapis woodi, named after Mr A.H.E. Wood of Aberdeenshire. But he notes wistfully that 'Pettigrew was the last Scot who wrote a book on bees'.

In 1756 Rev. Stephen White wrote 'Collateral bee boxes'. He was Rector at Holton in Suffolk. Nearly 100 years later Nutt was advocating the benefits of collateral (side-by-side) bee boxes and claiming the notion as his own!

It is instructive to notice the number of parsons and doctors of medicine who kept bees and graced the literature. Collectors with short purses might ponder the idea of limiting their collections to one or both of these callings. One wonders whether their interest is to be accounted for by their relative wealth, their leisure hours, their intellect or their natural sympathy with God's living creatures?

Certainly Dr. John Hill, in 1759 wrote the only book on honey itself prior to the twentieth century. He wrote much else on other subjects and was probably a quack who started out as an apothecary. Many books on the medicinal properties of honey have appeared since.

By now foreign influences were crossing the channel. John Mills' 'An essay in the management of bees' (1766) is derivative in its subject matter, but pays tribute to Mme Vicat and her hive, and to Reaumur.

Thomas Wildman, the next signpost to progress, was a relatively unschooled, but not unlettered showman and publicist, He made good use of Mills' book and shows a knowledge of French writers in producing his 'Treatise on bees' in 1768, now worth £250-300. He set himself up as the first bee expert, offering his services to owners of apiaries. He did tricks with swarms by controlling the queen, sometimes wearing them as a beard whilst riding a horse. He also wrote of wasps and hornets. There were two distinct 1768 editions, the second of which is often found bound up together with his 'Treatise upon peach trees'. A 2nd and 3rd edition followed (1770 and 1778).

His nephew Daniel also did tricks and like his uncle wrote a book. 'A complete guide to the management of bees....' first published in 1773 which ran to 20 editions. Neither his beekeeping, nor his tricks, nor his book seem to match the quality of his uncle. Nevertheless his book was done into German and Italian and was 'Americanised' under the authorship of 'A farmer of Massachusetts'. Daniel was an entrepreneur, a Holborn hive dealer, the first English professional beekeeping appliance-maker. Thorley's son, was also a dealer, 'but probably (as) a side line' (Fraser).

In 1771 William White of Banbury published 'A complete guide to the mystery and management of bees'. He was a professional beekeeper, and his work was attractive enough to be reprinted in 1852 together with a bee calendar by Beesley from the same town. This book was printed by J.G.Rusher in a special patented economical typeface without tails to the letters which makes it the more collectable. A facsimile was issued in 1977 by Northern Bee Books.

In 1776 Moses Harris, famous for his 'Aurelian', on butterflies, published 'An exposition of English Insects'. About four years later, it is estimated,Samuel Cooke produced a gardening book with 'The complete bee-master' added. It was a simple account of skep beekeeping, favouring killing the bees rather than driving them.

The call just then seems to have been for elementary texts. White and Cooke were followed by John Keys who, unlike most previous authors of major bee books has two titles to his name. He wrote 'The practical beemaster' while living in Hertfordshire (1780). He was probably a professional beekeeper like White, but he disputed Wildman's ideas and was sceptical of Schirach's revelation that queens could be raised from worker larvae. He moved to Bee Hall in Pembrokeshire where, in 1796, he wrote 'The antient bee-masters's farewell', with an addendum criticising James Bonner who supported Schirach's theory. Bee book collectors will note that authors spent much time and energy in disputing each other's theories. They should also take note that Keys' second book is not entitled 'an old beekeeper says goodbye' but rather 'A wise and experienced apiarist's successful do-it-yourself book' (farewell = get on successfully).

W. Dyer (1781) in an exceptionally rare book, 'The apiary laid open' advocated collateral boxes, like White before and Nutt later. Bryan J'Anson Bromwich (1783) wrote 'The experienced beekeeper'. He was a proponent of keeping more than one queen in a hive and collateral boxes, but he believed that wax was made from pollen.

James Bonner's (or Bonar's) first work was 'The bee-master's companion and assistant' of 1789. He knew that bees could raise queens from worker larvae. His second book, 'A new plan for speedily increasing the number of beehives in Scotland' ran to two editions in 1795 and '96. Walker calls him, 'The most able and best known of the Scottish bee-men'.

Inspired by Bromwich, Dr. Lettsom of Camberwell wrote a tract in 1796, with two editions that year: "Hints for promoting a bee society". This led to the formation of three societies, the only successful one being the 'Western Apiarian Society' which produced lively 'Transactions' for ten years from 1798. The Secretary, Jacob Isaac, wrote 'The general apiarian' (1799), with another edition in 1803.

So we conclude our canter through the greater bee books of the 18th century characterised in 'British Bee Books' as a hundred years of practical experience and scientific observation.

vi The Early Nineteenth Century
(Before Langstroth, 1852)

The 19th century saw enormous advances in technology. In 1803 the Fourdrinier machine was perfected at Hereford, the first to supersede the tray method of making paper by hand. On this machine liquid pulp flows onto a moving wire-mesh belt. In 1825 cloth was first used for publisher's bindings. In 1832 Leighton invented gold blocking on cloth. Mechanical composition of type was invented in 1822 and perfected in 1886, by which time woodpulp paper would be replacing that made from rags. With cloth coverings came cased bindings and enhanced decoration of covers. Bound books became rarer. The manufacture of books, in a word, became cheaper, and in consequence new titles proliferated. Accordingly the collector must consult the bibliography for the full record.

'British Bee Books' lists 261 entries during the nineteenth century contrasted with only 158 for the previous 200 years, many of which titles were only partly or incidentally concerned with bees.

With 'The life of a bee' by P.L. in 1800 a new genre of bee book makes its first appearance. It is a book written specifically for children. The standard bibliography for the scores of such books which follow is Natalie B. Hodgson's 'Children's books on bees and beekeeping'. Bees and their wonders, their industriousness, tidiness and perceived good citizenship have commended them to successive generations of writers who seize on them as examples in moral sermons or use their appeal to natural curiosity about the wonders of nature. 130 such books are listed in 'British Bee Books'. We shall come to them again later in this chapter.

Another characteristic of the nineteenth century is a paternalistic desire to help the poor to help themselves by keeping bees. Robert Huish, for example produced 'The cottager's manual' with this in mind in 1821 and there are numerous more or less condescending but well-intentioned books to follow on the same theme.

Collectors should also note that our forebears, both before and after 1800 tended to classify beekeeping as country-woman's work, along with poultry and domestic duties. Old Lawson issued his work on the husbandry of bees together with 'The country housewife's garden for hearbes of common use', and William Cobbett manages to unite both traditions in his 'Cottage economy: containing information relative to the brewing of beer, making of bread, keeping cows, pigs, bees ...etc.'

Another significant theme is a renewed readiness for scientific analysis, classification and recording. Various papers called 'The philosophical transactions of the Royal Society,' the findings of the microscopists, and works on natural history all demonstrate this interest. This was the period of Rev. Gilbert White's 'The natural history of Selbourne', (1789). The work of Linnaeus and other Europeans - Swammerdam, Reaumur, Maraldi and Schirach were all relatively recent. Oliver Goldsmith's 'History of the earth and animated nature' was being constantly reprinted. The 1st Edition of the 'Encyclopaedia Britannica' (1768) had details of 55 types of bee described by Linnaeus. The 4th edition (1800-1810) had an extensive account drawing on the well-known British and Continental authorities. William Kirby produced a masterpiece of early research 'Monographia apum angliae' in two volumes in 1802 which attempted to classify all the 'Linnean genus Apis as have been discovered in England' and lists the great names of English entomology from the late 18th century. Kirby and Spence – 'An introduction to entomology' – began in 1815 and eventually reached four volumes which were republished until 1885.

In 1806 the enormous advances in knowledge made possible by patient observation of bees by the blind Francis Huber and his colleague Francis Burnens was made available to English readers. Sir J.G. Dalzell's translation 'New observations on the natural history of bees' was published in Edinburgh. Huber's work first appeared in

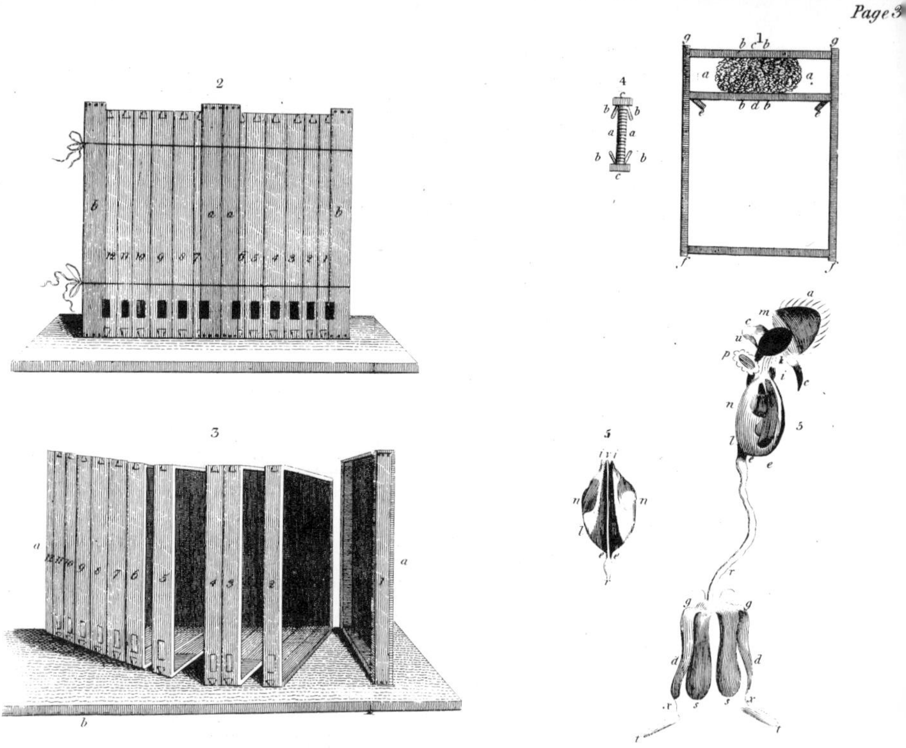

Page 300 - Francis Huber's leaf hive 1806.

Geneva in 1792. Five English editions were published to 1841. Huber's son Pierre added additional material in a new Parisian edition in 1814. The first full English edition is the Dadant American version of 1926. Huber it was who finally settled all arguments about the mating of queens and the origin of wax.

The next giant of bee literature was the impressive if not entirely attractive Robert Huish. He was misguided enough to challenge Huber's views. Kirby and Spence have judged Huber right and Huish wrong. He wrote, in 1815, 'A treatise on the nature, economy and practical management of bees' and two shorter works, instructions on his own hive, and the cottager's manual. His main book was successively enlarged through three more editions to 1844, and between whiles he wrote accounts of trials, romances, poems and moral tales. The book is a comprehensive study, the work of a practical skeppist and shows a sound knowledge of European ideas, in particular of their hives. Today a good 1st edition costs £100.

A notable curiosity of the period is 'Extracts on the natural history of bees' (1822) being extracts from Huber and Key [sic] by Roel (RObert RussELl). There were only two copies of the first edition and 20 of the second, 'A typographical curiosity' of 1834. Russell cut the

1

Page 13.

2

Page 23.

3

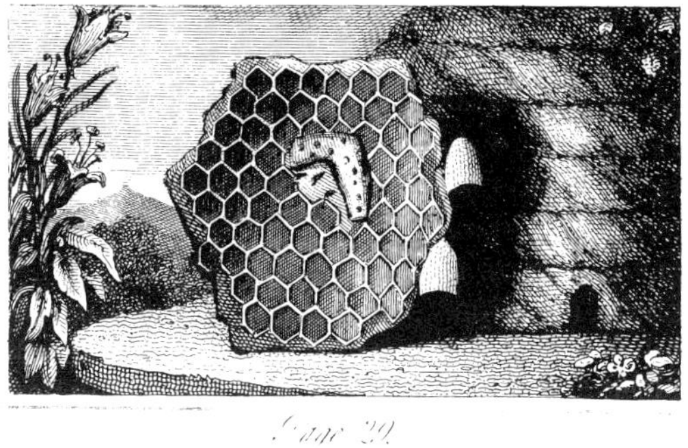

Page 29.

type himself and printed the book when he was only 15!

Dr. Edward Bevan produced 'The honey-bee' in 1827 which appeared in three editions. It was also published in the U.S.A., one of the earliest English bee books to find this new market. Howartson's work 'The apiarian's manual' (1827) is outclassed by Bevan's book, according to Walker. However he reckons it worthy of the tradition of the Scots Maxwell and Bonner.

Many notable entomologists were to follow with references to bees. Examples are 'The natural history of insects' of 1829, three works by James Rennie, a Scottish professor at Kings College, London in the early 1830's, Robert Patterson's 'Letters on the natural

10

Page 107.

11

Page 108.

12

Page 112.

history of insects mentioned in Shakespeare's plays' (1838), John Obadiah Westwood's 'The entomologist's handbook' of 1838 and his 'Introduction to the modern classification of insects' of 1839; 'The natural history of bees' (1840) by Rev. James Dunbar, part of 'The naturalists library', edited by Sir William Jardine. All appeared in just over a decade.

The flow of children's books grew in these years. Mr Frankly's 'The history of Frugal, the wild bee' of 1817 is an early example. Maria Hack (1821) wrote 'Harry Beaufoy'. In 1827 Mrs Johnstone gave us 'Scenes of industry' for the delectation of the young and in 1832 Lydia Child's 'The girls own book' was issued, to be republished in

16

Page 121.

17

Page 125.

18

Page 127.

Illustrations from the 2nd edition of Mrs Johnstone's 'Scenes of Industry' 1830.

numerous editions down to 1876 for reading on both sides of the Atlantic.

In 1832/3 there appeared:

'Mamma's lessons for her little boys and girls'

'Insect histories for children'

'Insects and their habitations'

'The wonderful history of the busy bees'

Those keen to collect such works should follow up this brief introduction by consulting Hodgson.

The urge to help the rural poor, usually called 'cottagers'

Children's books of yesterday and today.

increased. 'British Bee Books' lists 23 such titles. But Bevan made an exception of himself, carefully pointing out that his book was intended for 'the more intelligent members of the community'! He meant that his work was to be deemed authoritative in scientific and practical terms rather than a self-help manual. These 'simple' books were often couched in language which would have been difficult for the unlettered poor who lived before the 1870 Education Act, however unsophisticated the beekeeping lore may have been. J.H. Payne's 'Cottagers Guide' of 1832 was given away in East Anglia. William Chamber's 'Cottage economy (1833) was often reprinted. W.C. Cotton produced, in 1837, 'A short and simple letter to cottagers' and another later which reappeared in his scrapbook anthology of 1842 'My bee book' just prior to his leaving, with his bees, for New Zealand. Richard Smith issued 'The cottager's bee book' in 1839 and in the following year came 'The cottage bee-hive' by A. Beekeeper. The theme continues throughout the century.

The collector may care to keep in mind the audiences that various authors were targeting as they put pen to paper. Throughout the history of bee-writing these have included children, beginners, hobbyists, knowledgeable scientists, general readers with a philosophical, poetic, moralistic or even religious turn of mind, small farmers intent on profitability and latterly serious students and examination candidates. Cooks, wine-makers, healthy eaters and gardeners can also constitute a specific audience, while a few works,

Great titles of the nineteenth century.

like this one are aimed at historians and bibliophiles.

Alternatively the collector may care to look at his personal categorisation of bee-books not from the putative audience but rather from the characteristics of the authors. We have already noted the propensity for medical men and parsons to write about their pastime. To them must be added school teachers, lecturers, county bee advisers and similar bee-wise professionals in local or national government posts. In recent times bee-farmers like Simmins,R.O.B. Manley and Oliver Field have offered both memoires and advice. In the mid 19th century, the heyday of the entrepreneur, the enterprising bee-equipment manufacturer, hive-maker and retailer had a vested interest in supporting his products with an authoritative book.

We have already noticed this with the Wildman's - Daniel the nephew being the first true example of the dealer-author. In 1823 John Milton (the apiarist, not the puritan) wrote 'The London apiarian guide for bee-keepers' - 'Published at the Apiarian Repository, 175 Strand, where the finest honey, and hives of every description may be had'. His 'Practical beekeeper' appeared in 1843. He used some of W.C.Cotton's notes in this book. Cotton seems to have been incensed about it on his return from New Zealand. They disappear from the 1851 edition!

We shall pick up the theme of the dealer-author later.

vii 1850. Langstroth rules

The general flow of bee-books rolled along until mid-century when the great revolution in beekeeping methods began in the U.S.A. with Langstroth's discovery of the bee-space and the moveable frame hive.

The bee-book collector with an interest in the historical development of the craft may trace the slow build-up of knowledge over centuries, identifying the pieces of the jig-saw which Langstroth dropped into place to create a new image of beekeeping in 1851.

There had long been a strong humanitarian tradition in bee-writing which expressed the secret guilt of the skeppists and box-hive men who killed their bees in autumn to take the honey. Gerard, Thorley, Maxwell, S. White, Mills, Petrie, Strutt, J.H. Payne, Keys, Isaac, Huish, Gelieu, Nutt, Cotton and Scudamore – all had debated ways of taking honey and preserving the bees by driving, narcotics or hive designs which separated the broodnest box from jars, collateral boxes or supers where honey might be stored. Beekeepers were ready for a breakthrough.

The design of bars from which combs might hang, and of frames which might give shape to those combs had a long gestation. Sir George Wheler (1682) reported on Greek skeps with moveable bars. In the following year A.J. (possibly John Aubry) described a wooden hive with moveable frames. Huber (1806) made a contribution with his leaf hive, and Howatson (1827), following Huber, 'designed an excellent bar-hive'. William Munn (1844) wrote 'A description of the bar-and-frame hive' which anticipated some of Langstroth's discoveries and was used in a lawsuit to contest the American's patent.

1851, the year of the Great Exhibition, is a key date in beekeeping when Langstroth, descended from a family of the Yorkshire Dales, made a moveable frame that could actually be moved.('The Life of Langstroth' F. Naile, Cornell Univ. Press 1942.) When Mehring invented wax foundation in 1857 the die was cast. Subsequent inventions-the queen excluder, the smoker, the bee escape and the centrifugal extracter would follow so that the old order would change, giving place to new.

Nevertheless the second half of the 19th century did not see an immediate crop of modernists making clarion calls to fellow beekeepers to adopt the new hive. Indeed in many ways the publications follow familiar patterns with more children's books, entomological works and booklets for cottagers. Some examples were:

'A country curate' [Filleul] 1851

'The hive and its wonders' Cross 1852

'Bees, their habits, management and treatment' by the popularist Rev. J.G. Wood 1853

THE HIVE AND ITS WONDERS

See page 81.

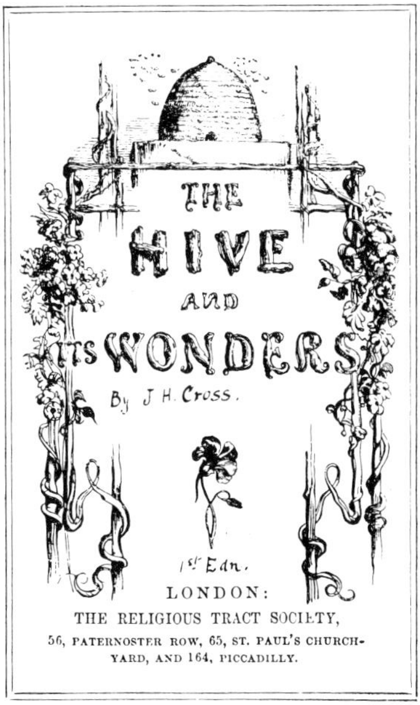

THE
HIVE
AND
ITS WONDERS
By J. H. Cross.
1st Edn.
LONDON:
THE RELIGIOUS TRACT SOCIETY,
56, PATERNOSTER ROW, 65, ST. PAUL'S CHURCH-YARD, AND 164, PICCADILLY.

By

A. L. O. E.,

Author of "The Silver Casket," "The Crown of Success," &c.

WITH ILLUSTRATIONS FROM DESIGNS BY W. HARVEY, ESQ.

"How doth the little busy bee
Improve each shining hour,
And gather honey all the day
From every opening flower!"
WATTS.

LONDON:
T. NELSON AND SONS, PATERNOSTER ROW:
EDINBURGH; AND NEW YORK.
1864.

Improving books for children of the nineteenth century.

'Beekeeping for the many' J.H. Payne 1853

'Wings and stings' by A.L.O.E. (A lady of England) 1855

'The Italian Alp bee' by H.C. Herman 1860 marking the first introduction of Italian bees to England.

The magisterial work of Charles Darwin 'On the origin of species by means of natural selection' appeared in 1859, and though there are references to pollination it can hardly be described as a bee-book. Nevertheless it symbolises aptly the science in men's minds which was spilling over into the natural history of bees and the technology of bee-craft. Also to be included among the notable bee titles were two by Samuel Orchart Beeton - 'The book of home pets' and 'The book of garden management' (1861-2). Beeton was husband to Mrs Beeton, whose book on household management has become a household noun.

The first author in Britain to propagate Langstroth's ideas was T.W. Woodbury who wrote 'Bees and beekeeping' in 1862, treating of the Ligurian bee. His various 'bar and frame hives' with wood or straw walls are well publicised in Neighbour's 'The apiary' of 1865, offered for sale 'complete with outside cover and super £3-10-0'. At this price there was no immediate incentive for poorer folk to modernise their methods. The advocates of skeps still persisted.

It was not until 1882, when the British Standard frame-size was established that any consistency came to frame designs. As late as 1870 Pettigrew wrote his 'Handy book of bees' championing large skeps as the best mode of working. But Piers Edgcombe Martin in 'The great Hampshire bee farm' of 1878 is equally strong on 'The standard bar-frame hive for the United Kingdom' - the sailors' beehive. Simmins in 'A modern bee farm' 1887 further authenticated the moveable frame principle with his commercial hive.

Mention of Neighbour's 'The Apiary' and P.E. Martin recalls the contribution to bee-letters from the entrepreneurs. In 1863 Wyatt J. Pettit of Dover who made and sold equipment put out a booklet. 'The management of bees' – recommended by John Cumming, 'The Times' Beemaster' in 'Beekeeping' (1864). The following year Alfred Neighbour, son of George, a notable manufacturer, produced his collectable book, which ran to three editions. The Neighbours exhibited at the Great Exhibition of 1851. Alfred was himself a bee-book collector. He bought up Tegetmeier's collection and sold it to Colonel Walker. Tegetmeier was a founder member of the Royal Entomological Society who wrote in 'The Field' till he was 90.

Alfred Rusbridge who made and sold equipment promised 100 - 300% profit on capital invested in keeping bees in 'A book for beekeepers' (1875) and 'Beekeeping, plain and practical' (1883). Thomas Blow, founder of the Welwyn firm which became Taylors, issued a catalogue 'Bees, hives and honey' in 1886 which is now very valuable. Taylors 'Bee appliances and how to use them' (1901) reflects

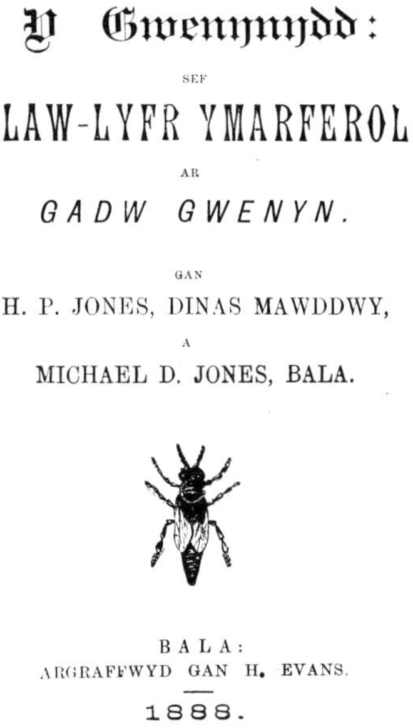

Y Gwenynydd:

SEF

LLAW-LYFR YMARFEROL

AR

GADW GWENYN.

GAN

H. P. JONES, DINAS MAWDDWY,

A

MICHAEL D. JONES, BALA.

BALA:
ARGRAFFWYD GAN H. EVANS.

1888.

HYSBYSIADAU. 121

Mae ein Tyniedydd yn well nag un arall. Sylwer ar y gwobrwyon a enillwyd.

Mae y ddyfais hon yn cario'r blaen ar bob un arall, a chydnabyddir mai hwn ydyw'r goreu fel Cwch defnyddiol, ac ar yr un pryd yn Gwch Gwydr i weled y gwenyn yn gweithio.

D.S.—Dychwelir yr arian os na cheir boddhad digonol.

JOHN H. HOWARD,
Practical Manufacturer,
The Model Apiary, Holme, Nr. Peterboro.

'Y gwenywydd' (The Beekeeper) of 1888 – The first bee book in Welsh.

the change of ownership. Hasluck, in 1905, edited a general work, 'Beehives and beekeepers appliances' which summarised the equipment of the period.

The tradition has continued in modern times, most notably in the USA where the Dadant and A.I. Root companies have produced encyclopaedic works ('The ABC of beekeeping' and 'The hive and the honey bee') as a regular series.

From this point it becomes impossible to point out all the collectable titles that have been published in a work of this kind. A few key names are:

Siebold	'On a true parthenogenesis'	1857
Shuckard	'British bees'	1866
Edwards	'The French bishop's advice'	1871
Busch	'Buzz a buzz' (Trans. Cotton)	1872
Cheshire	'Practical beekeeping	1873
	'Bees and beekeeping' Scientific Vol.I.	1886
	Practical Vol.II.	1888
Hunter	'A manual of beekeeping'	1875
British Beekeeping		1880-
Association	'Modern beekeeping' 9 eds.	1904
Robinson	'British bee-farming'	1880

Cowan	'British bee-keepers guide book' 25 Eds.	1881-1924
	'The honey-bee'	1890
Dzierzon	'Dzierzon's rational beekeeping' (the discoverer of parthenogenesis)	1882
Lubbock	'Ants, bees and wasps'	1882
Jenyns	'A book about the bees' (Children's book with an illustration of a cottager with skeps and moveable frames)	1886
Jones and Jones	'Y gwenynydd' 'The beekeeper' The first book in Welsh 1888	1888
Webster	'The book of bee-keeping - 8 editions	1888-1947
Samson	'Bees for pleasure and profit - 5 editions	1892
Saunders	'The hymenoptera aculeata of the British Isles'	1896

Here endeth the nineteenth century.

viii 1900 The Twentieth Century

Our cataclysmic and almost time-expired century had run three-quarters of its days in 1976 when 'British bee Books' appeared. In those 76 years the number of titles listed is almost exactly the same as that for the previous four hundred years.

Population growth, advanced printing technology and popular education must have played their part, for it is unlikely that the number of hives or beekeepers increased during this period. Knowledge of bee anatomy, beekeeping technique, bee behaviour and beekeeping history together prompted an average of five new books a year in Britain alone, and this pattern shows every sign of continuing.

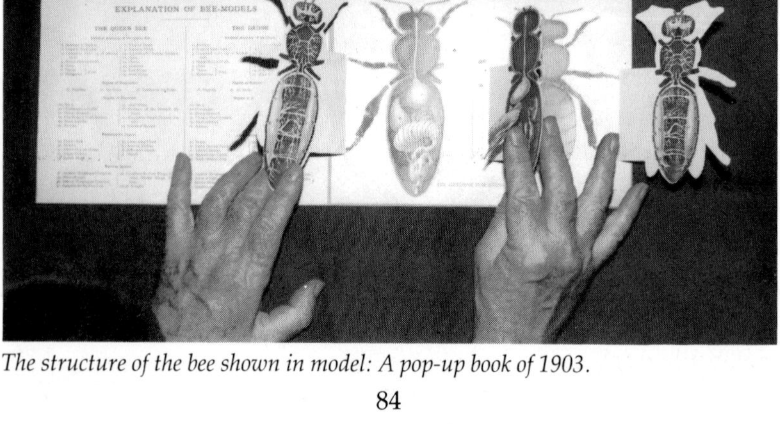

The structure of the bee shown in model: A pop-up book of 1903.

Beekeeping journals and ephemera.

Some titles and some authors proved enduring and authoritative, certain works going into numerous editions and certain bee-men going into print on several occasions. The majority on the other hand, were ephemeral works and their authors are not respected by posterity. However, being out-of- print and rare, such works may still be sought out by the collector.

The following list is no substitute for the bibiography. It names the authors and titles best known either by their popularity or their influence. Books for children, though numerous, are omitted.

Maeterlinck	'The life of the bee'	1901
	beekeeping's one literary work.	
	Numerous editions.	
Rev. J. Digges	'The Irish bee guide'	1904
	Subsequently 'The practical bee guide'	1910
	which ran to 15 editions to 1950.	
Rev. Tickner		1905-
Edwardes	Seven novels and instructional works.	1926
T. Cowan	Seven titles	1881-1928

Cowan's work was enormously influential, particularly the 'Guide book'. He was a founder member of the British Beekeepers Association and helped guide its fortunes for nearly half a century. 'The British Bee Journal' which he edited, is of interest to collector and historian alike, and can be found collected and bound in annual volumes.

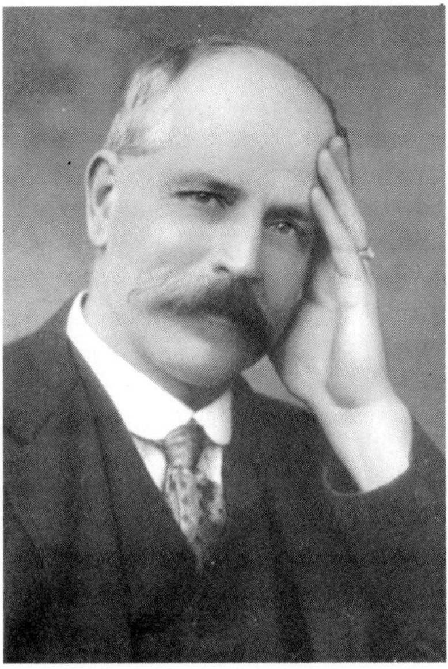

Author's portraits
Huber Langstroth
Cowan Herrod-Hempsall

Mace

Henry Geary	'Profitable bee-keeping for small holders and others - 5 editions	1911-1923
William Herrod-Hempsall	Seven titles	1912-1938

This man epitomised bee-keeping expertise and dominated the world of beekeeping up to the second World War. His 'Beekeeping new and old, described with pen and camera' of 1930 (Vol.1) and 1937 (Vol.2) is a comprehensive work, the biggest and most all- embracing study so far published. No serious collector can be without it, and must pay £250 for both volumes. Volume 1 is commoner and therefore much cheaper.

L.E. Snelgrove	Five titles 1912- He wrote up his work on queens and swarm control.	1946
Frank C. Pellett	'Productive bee keeping' – in four editions.	1916
Herbert Mace	Eleven titles	1921-1952
A.B. Flower	'Beekeeping up-to-date' Six editions to 1952	1925
Brother Adam	1964 to date.	
D.V. Alford	'Bumblebees'	1975
C.G. Butler	Five titles from 1948 including 'The world of the honeybee' No.29 in The New Naturalist series.	
H.A. Dade	'Anatomy and dissection of the honeybee' The most useful book for students.	1962
Alexander Deans	Four titles 1949-1963	
Malcolm H. Fraser	Three titles of historical and bibliographical interest including	1931-1958

Modern beebooks for students and general readers.

Works by Herbert Mace.

	'History of beekeeping in Britain' 1958.	
John Free	(with Butler) Bumblebees and subsequent scientific work.	1959
Von Frisch	Translations of this most influential writer, recording the results of study of bee behaviour.	1950
G.R. Gayre	'Wassail! in mazers of mead' The celebratory book on honey drinks.	1948
Dorothy Hodges	'The pollen loads of the honeybee'	1952

M.M. Hooper	'Common Sense beekeeping' Four editions to 1948	1939
Ted. Hooper	'Guide to bees and honey'	1976
	and 'Encyclopedia of beekeeping' (with Roger Morse) by today's leading practical expert.	1985
F.N. Howes	'Plants and beekeeping' The fullest work on bee forage.	1945
R.O.B. Manley	Three titles. Bee-farming and practical experience.	1936-1948
Hilda Ransome	'The sacred bee in ancient times and folklore'. Scarce and collectable.	1937
C.R. Ribbands	'The behaviour and social life of honeybees'. A scientific work still of interest to students.	1953
E.S. Rohde	'Shakespeare's wild flowers' Includes bee lore.	1937
H.J. Wadey	Three titles	1943-1948
H.J.O. Walker	'Descriptive catalogue of bee books	1929

A valuable work listing all of Walker's great collection, now in the Miller Library in Wisconsin. Walker had edited the catalogue of the BBKA first issued in 1882 and reissued in 1912.

E.B. Wedmore	'A manual of beekeeping' and three other titles.	1932

Several of the above titles are in print and there are scores of books published since 1976 which are still available as new titles or can be supplied second-hand by dealers. The wise collector will make sure he has first editions of modern works on his shelves. Certain books turn out to be classics and are reissued many times. Those that have a short print-run in the first place, and do not quite merit a reprint because of the limited scope of the market can soon become scarce and costly. This is most likely to be true of more learned works on scientific aspects of beekeeping. These books tend to be expensive when new because of their recondite nature.

The International Bee Research Association issues catalogues of books in print.

11.
Books Published Overseas

American Works

The bee book collector must make a decision on how to treat American books at an early point in his collecting. He may well decide to exclude them unless they are actually published or jointly published in the U.K. It is now difficult to categorise a book by its place of printing since this is a multi-national matter with much printing being done overseas on contract.

Some examples of books in this category are T.B. Miner 'The American beekeepers manual' published both in London and the U.S.A. in 1849 with four subsequent editions. The definitive work by Dr. J.A. Nelson 'The embryology of the honey bee' came out in Princeton and the OUP in 1915 and 'The anatomy of the honey bee' 1925 (R.E. Snodgrass) was jointly published in 1956. Any British collection would be the worse for the omission of these American standard works.

However the works of Dadant, Root , Langstroth, Quimby and Doolittle do not qualify by this criterion, being imported rather than published in Britain.

Another demarcation question arises over British titles published in the USA or elsewhere. The collector may need to establish a policy as to including them or not. We must assume that most early American books in the colonial period, like the honeybee itself* were imported from Europe. According to Johansson in the introduction to "Apicultural literature published in Canada and the United States" (1972), which is the standard bibliography, Langstroth is known to have quoted Butler and sent copies of Keys and Wildman to Root.

The first 'All American' bee-book was produced by Isaiah Thomas in 1792. But "A complete guide.... by a farmer of Massachusetts" was really the work of Daniel Wildman, plagiarised.

Johansson lists only ten American titles before 1821, one of which was ' A short history of bees' (1803) published anonymously in England in 1800 and based on Reaumur. Up to 1852, the time of Langstroth, he cites only 30 more publications.

Undoubtedly the issue of Dr. Bevan's 'The honey bee' in 1843, which was a reprint of the 1838 2nd English edition had a significant influence on Langstroth's thought, especially because Robert Golding, who collaborated with Bevan, made experiments and observations which led him to the idea of the moveable frame.

Another significant English work was the American reprint of the 6th edition of Kirby and Spence - 'An introduction to entomology' in 1846.

*[believed to be 1638 A.D.]

"NOVICE'S"

Gleanings in Bee Culture.

1873

Or how to Realize the Most Money with the Smallest Expenditure of Capital and Labor in the Care of Bees, Rationally Considered.

PUBLISHED QUARTERLY.

VOL. I. MEDINA, O., JAN 1, 1873. No. 1

INTRODUCTORY.

FELLOW NOVICES —We must confess to a feeling of not being quite as much at home here, just yet, as in the old *American Bee Journal*, but we trust we shall *all*, in time, feel all the liberty here that we have there enjoyed. Remember at all times that Improved Bee Culture is our end and aim, and we trust no one will hesitate to give any facts from experience, because they may tend to overthrow any particular person or "hobby."

If any of *our* especial plans don't work, or if any thing we advertise has had its value over-estimated, here in these pages is the place of all others to set the error right. Please don't be hasty or prematurely positive, and when one of our number acknowledges a fault and makes proper reparation, the matter should be overlooked and friendly feelings renewed on both sides, at once and forever

The advances now being made in Bee Culture, it seems to us, must necessarily bring about *individual* losses often, for instance, one of us may have made up a quantity of hives for sale, and new developments may point out plainly that they are not fully adapted to the present needs of Bee Culture, and when you are satisfied of this, please do not attempt to sell them without telling your customer the *whole truth*, and making the price correspond The same may be said of Extractors. If necessary to throw them away as old lumber or old metals, do not, we implore you, hesitate an instant.

Our most successful business men of the present day, have discovered it to be a fact that it is more profitable to tell their customers the *bad points* of their wares as well as the good There are ample opportunities in this world to acquire a competence *honestly*

One of the most lamentable wrongs in Bee Culture is the custom of taking money for a "right to make and use" a hive, knowing that the buyer could "make and use" a hive so nearly like it as to answer every purpose, without using a SINGLE ONE OF THE PATENTED FEATURES It will be our especial aim to fully inform the public of all such transactions coming under our observation

Please give facts all you can without regard to their bearing on individuals, if they are of such a nature as to benefit the masses Without further moralizing we will try and let our little JOURNAL show for itself what it is, but, dear readers, we hope you have read this carefully for we may refer to it hereafter

Reproduction of the first page of *Gleanings*, 1873 — B. K. Jan., 1939

Reproduction of the first page of 'Gleanings' 1873 - B.K. Jan. 1939.

After Langstroth books abounded as the American beekeeping fraternity flourished and the honey and pollination industries waxed prosperous under the benign influence of his boxes with moveable frames.

Langstroth's 'Hive and the honey bee' first appeared in 1853 and the title has continued to be reedited ever since. Likewise A.I. Root's 'ABC of bee culture' of 1877 has been constantly redrafted and translated into several languages.

Moses Quinby, who improved the design of the smoker, wrote 'Mysteries of bee-keeping explained' in 1853 which was reissued many times to 1908. Quinby is said to have owned 1200 hives in New York State.

Other notable names the collector of American bee-books might seek are those of: H. Alley (five titles) particularly on queen rearing. A.J. Cook ('Manual of the apiary' 1876 and 19 subsequent editions). G.M. Doolittle (five titles) notably on grafting queens. J. Hoffman ('Treatise on bees' 1853), Dadant's translation of Huber (1926). NH and HA King. 1864, 'The bee keeper's text book.' 27 editions to 1888. C.C. Miller from 1874 - 7 titles. T. Newman from 1877 - 9 titles. J.W. Pagden (1868?) - '$350 a year: How I make it with my bees'. F.C. Pellett from 1916 - 13 titles. especially 'American honey plants' of 1920. 'Productive bee-keeping' 1916 and 'Beginners bee book' 1919 were both published in London by Lippincott. Dr.E.F. Phillips (five titles). Macmillans produced 'Beekeeping' in London in 1915 at the

Well-known titles from the U.S.A.

height of the Great War.

Johansson lists 613 American titles to 1972, 27 Canadian books, 67 Canadian Provincial works, 167 US Federal publications and about 25 sides of closely typed listings of books published in individual American states.

The ambitious collector of American books must either be selective in some disciplined way, of hire a large warehouse and get possession of a deep purse. The one economical factor is the absence of truly antiquarian works. However the true 'American collector' will consider all early books published in Europe to be part of the American heritage, and seek them out.

It should be in no way surprising that H.J.O.Walker's great collection went to Madison, USA.

12.
Books Translated into English

The British bee-book collector has to make mental provision for other European works. He may decide to collect important foreign authors in their original language. Alternatively he may choose to collect good early translations.

Since the classical writers were the earliest 'authorities' on beekeeping the earnest collector will look for them. Pliny (Philomon Holland 1601) is an early example. The 2nd edition made £160 in 1986. Virgil is important – 'Eclogues with his booke De apibus', translated by J. Brinsley, 1620; 'works' translated John Ogilby 1649 with reference to bees in the Fourth Georgic, and by Dryden, 1697.

Columella's 'Of husbandry' was translated by Curtius in·1745. Varro's 'Three books concerning agriculture' were translated by Rev. Owen in 1800.

Possibly of greater apiarian interest however will be the tracing of continental influences into English bee letters. It would be naive to suppose that England was ever politically or socially insular. Feudal aristocracy and royalty were more loyal to their social class than their nation states. International trade and the free traffic of ideas were less 'protected' than we may imagine. The English national stock has been built up and bred from European predators.

John Fitzherbert (1523) sounds like a Norman. 'The Grete Herball' (1526) was translated from the French. Hill's book of 1568 was 'Englished' from a German's work in Latin and Heresbach's 'Four bookes of husbandrie' were translated, from a work published in Cologne four years earlier, by Barnaby Googe.

Though Southerne's book was 'according to his own experience', and many similar works were to follow, it is true to say that a large number of works were directly or indirectly influenced from abroad. Butler's work, of course, was distinctive enough to take the opposite path, being translated into Latin for international reading.

Leewenhoeck's work on bees was made known to the Royal Society in 1673. Richard Bradley made use of Maraldi's work in his 'General treatise on husbandry' and he also translated Chomel's 'Dictionnaire oeconnomique' in 1725. Noel Pluche was translated into English by Samuel Humphries in 1733, and in 1744 Bazin's 'The natural history of bees' appeared in English. The substance of this book came from Reaumur.

We know that Arthur Dobbs (1750) had read Reaumur and seen Swammerdam's 'Biblia natura' which was not done into English until 1758 as 'The book of nature'. Thomas Floyd translated it from Dutch and Latin, and had it improved by notes from Reaumur, written by John Hill.

The collector can continue to trace this interaction of continental scientists and English writers. By 1800 the Encyclopaedia Britannica had references to Maraldi, Reaumur, Pluche, Swammerdam, Schirach and the Abbe Boissier. In 1806 Englishmen were able to read Huber's book fourteen years after its publication in French.

Other names to note in translation are:

Gelieu (1829) 'The bee preserver'
Siebold (1857) 'On parthenogenesis'
Figuier (1868) 'The insect world'
Busch (1872) 'Buzz a buzz' - a poem.
Michelet (1875) 'The insect.
Ribeaucourt (1879) 'A manual of rational beekeeping'
Dzierzon (1882) 'Parthenogenesis in bees'
Fabre (1901) 'Insect life'
Maeterlinck (1901) 'The life of the bee'

By the turn of the century the attention of bee-keepers throughout the world was focussed on the U.S.A. Langstroth's revolution and the dominance of his hive and its derivatives, linked with the internationalisation of information meant that major individual influences were less readily discernible.

However the work of Von Frisch in the '50s and '60s shows that significant discoveries and revelations are still possible from any source in the world.

13.

Bee Books as Literature

The majority of bee authors would be long forgotten had their subject not been beekeeping. It is the intrinsic interest of what they had to say, correct or erroneous as it may have been, rather than the felicity of their style which has caused posterity to remember them.

Many had grace and skill with words. The clerks in Holy orders and the doctors were necessarily well read and dealt in rhetoric. Warder and Thorley may stand as examples.

Many were of a philosophical turn of mind. It is arguable that contemplating bees is both cause and effect of a meditative temperament. Others were traders, dealers in equipment, and their style may be moved by the rhetoric of the advertiser. Such language may not be poetic but it is adroit in its persuasiveness. Often enough they are able people of their time moved to letters by the urge to share their enthusiasm with others. Their prose is charged with their commitment, an assurance sometimes bordering on the opinionated. As intelligent literate persons their writings are characteristic of their period.

In all these diverse ways they may hold an interest for the modern reader. But only a few books will find a larger readership outside the ranks of students of the history of language or of beekeeping.

Among authors who might attract a wider audience are these:

Thomas Tusser	'A hundreth good pointes of husbandrie' (1557), a work in verse which was expanded into '500 points' in 1573.
Charles Butler	'The feminine monarchy' 1609. The work of a musician and scholar with a great interest in the use and grammar of language.
John Day	'The parliament of bees' An early example of a political satire in verse. Its date (1641) places it right amidst the turmoil of the Civil War.
Samuel Purchas	'A theatre of politicall flying-insects' 1657, meditations and observations theological and moral.
Samuel Pepys and John Evelyn	The famous diarists whose works need no recommendation. Evelyn's manuscript on bees from 'Elysium Britannicum' was reprinted in 1966.
John Dryden	Verse translation of 'The Works of Virgil' 1697

Bernard de Mandeville	'The fable of the bees' 1714, another political satire.
John Gay	'Fables'. The author of 'The beggar's opera' addressed fable X 'The degenerate bees' to Dean Swift, the author of 'Gullivers Travels'. The corrupt bee was probably Horace Walpole.
Cosmo	'Makarony Fables' 1768. Another satire.
Oliver Goldsmith	'A history of the earth' 1774
Gilbert White	'The natural history of Selbourne' 1789. A famous work of literature with a well-known anecdote of an idiot boy who ate bees.
John Evans	1806. A poem in four books of which three were published.
William Cobbett	'Cottage economy' 1822 - the work of the author of 'Rural Rides'
Leigh Hunt	'A jar of honey from Mount Hybla'. "A mixture of old Sicilian story and English pastoral" (British Bee Books)
J. Fenimore Cooper	'The beehunter' 1848 - author of 'Last of the Mohicans'.
Mrs Alfred Gatty	'Parables from nature' 1855. Later collected editions of her work are illustrated by Holman Hunt, Burne-Jones, Weir and Tenniel.
Charles Darwin	'Origin of Species' 1859
Wilhelm Busch	'Buzz a buzz' 1872 - comic verse.
Maurice Maeterlinck	'The life of the bee' 1901 and 'The children's life of the bee' 1920. This is the classic of bee literature.
Rev. Tickner Edwardes	'The beemaster of Warrilow' 1907 and 'The lore of the honey bee' 1908, Sussex's answer to Maeterlinck! "But more accurate" according to Walker.

And finally:

A.A. Milne	'Winnie the Pooh' 1926.

Art in bee books: Kit Williams, Detmold Graham Sutherland, and the engraved frontispiece to Worlidge's "Systema Agriculturæ."

14.
Recent Twentieth Century Bee Books

There have been numerous books on bee themes since the first world war intended for the amusement and delight of the reader rather than his instruction.

Whether or not any such books in the following list will qualify the hundred year test of real literature is highly questionable, but they may all be read with pleasure and interest by bee-keeping enthusiasts.

Two books by artists may well prove valuable assets. They are Kit Williams' untitled book from 1984 and Graham Sutherland's book of aquatints called 'bees'.

Bonsels	Maya: The adventures of a little bee 1922
Evrard	The mystery of the hive 1925
Abbot	Me and the bee 1965
Bell	The joys of beekeeping 1932
Buhet	The honey seige 1953
Buzzard	Shining hours 1946
Coryn	A swarm of bees 1947
Dunning	The key of the hive 1945
Francon	The mind of the bees 1939
Heard	A taste of honey 1942
Herzog	The swarm - filmed 1974
Kelsey	The spell of the hive 1945
Lisney	The bee walk 1953
Lund	A man and his bees 1947
Morgan	The revolt of the bees 1926
Pim	A hive of suspects 1952
Pythian	The bee garden 1933
Ratcliffe	Beekeepers folly 1949
Rendle	The way of a bee 1933
Stratton-Porter	Keeper of the bees 1929
Stuart	City of the bees 1947
Teale	The golden throng 1942
Tennant	The honey flow-Australian 1956
Vivian (really Ashley)	The singing masons 1950
Wadey	The behaviour of bees and beekeepers 1948
Weightman	The border bees 1961
Williams	The story of the hive 1928

There have been several anthologies of bee literature which make diverting reading –

My bee book - Cotton (reprint)
A murmur of bees – Amoret Scott 1980
Curiosities of bee-keeping – L.Croft 1989

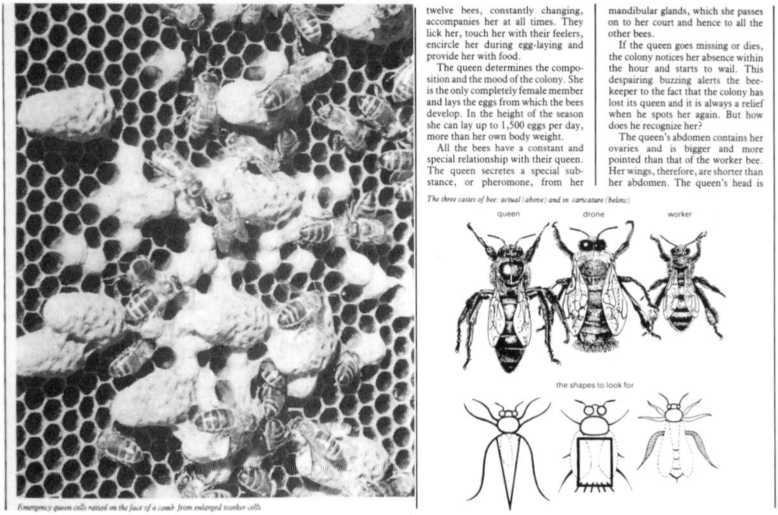

twelve bees, constantly changing, accompanies her at all times. They lick her, touch her with their feelers, encircle her during egg-laying and provide her with food.

The queen determines the composition and the mood of the colony. She is the only completely female member and lays the eggs from which the bees develop. In the height of the season she can lay up to 1,500 eggs per day, more than her own body weight.

All the bees have a constant and special relationship with their queen. The queen secretes a special substance, or pheromone, from her mandibular glands, which she passes on to her court and hence to all the other bees.

If the queen goes missing or dies, the colony notices her absence within the hour and starts to wail. This despairing buzzing alerts the beekeeper to the fact that the colony has lost its queen and it is always a relief when he spots her again. But how does he recognize her?

The queen's abdomen contains her ovaries and is bigger and more pointed than that of the worker bee. Her wings, therefore, are shorter than her abdomen. The queen's head is

The three castes of bee: actual (above) and in caricature (below)

Emergency queen cells raised on the face of a comb from enlarged worker cells

English edition: Irmgard Diemer 'Bees and beekeeping' 1988

Because of the enormous strides made since the war it is among the titles of the last two decades that the finest photographic reproductions, the most accessible guides for beginners and the most erudite works of science are to be found. Modern books may lack the beauty of handsomely bound antiquarian volumes, but they have qualities of design and illustration which can give enormous pleasure. The inquisitive beekeeper, keen to know more of the science and practice of his craft must make them his study. Many nuggets of wisdom are to be found in the older texts, nor were myths, superstitions and half-truths the monopoly of the ancients. Those kinds of disinformation still continue. But the received wisdom of generations of sound practice and recent research make modern authoritative texts reliable, if not impeccable.

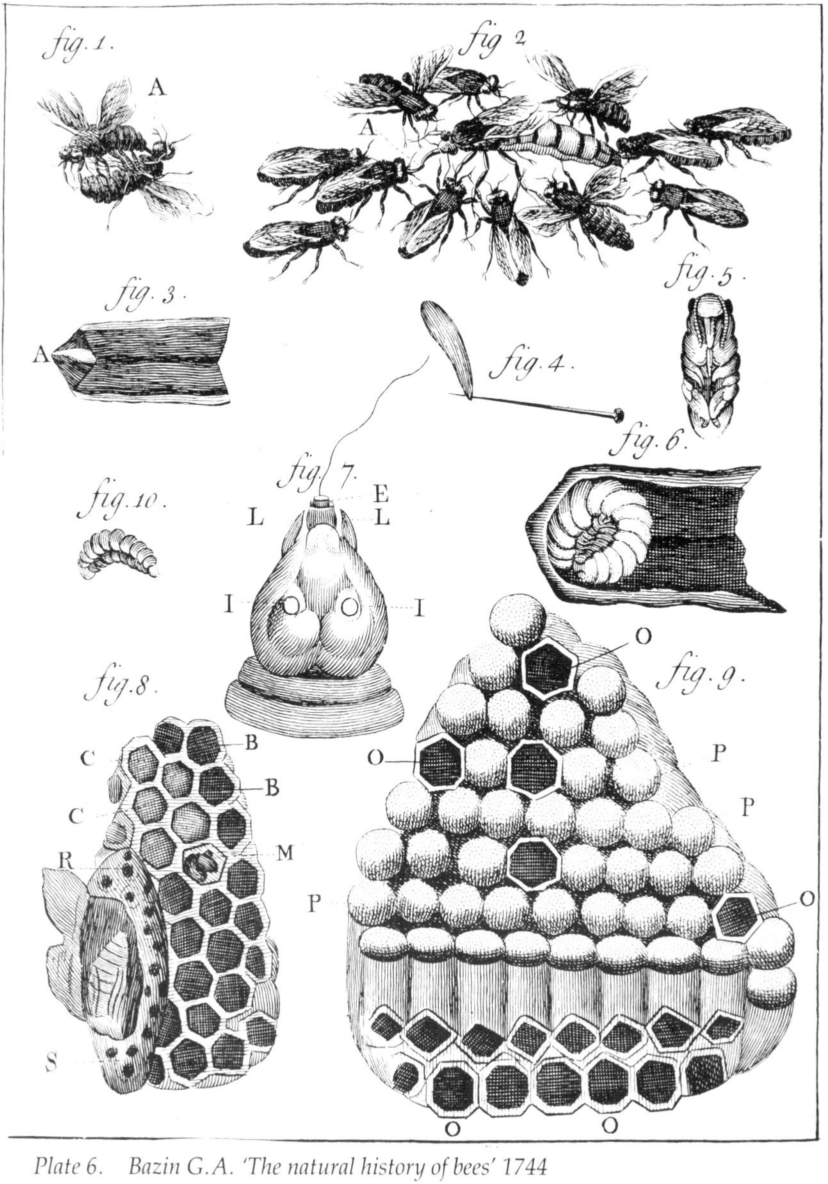

Plate 6. *Bazin G.A. 'The natural history of bees' 1744*

15.
Ephemera

Papers on bees and beekeeping intended by their authors to do service for a day or a season and then to be discarded, will, with the passage of years, become firstly matters of curiosity to a later generation, and ultimately historical documents of great value to collectors.

Often old and rare books will contain letters from beekeepers long dead, plans of new hives, bills and receipts for equipment, pamphlets and notes. Sometimes they might prove more valuable than the book they are found in.

Old catalogues, learned papers, minutes of early bee societies, copies of 'British Bee Journal' and 'Bee World' of early date, newspaper articles, advertisements used by equipment dealers, honey jar labels, rules for honey shows and so forth all deserve careful preservation.

Yesterday's rubbish that escaped the waste paper basket is today's prize specimen, with pride of place in the collector's filing cabinet.

170

1895 **Buckeridge (H. A.) A set of 6 humorous illustrations depicting the misfortunes of an angler stung by bees,** ? executed in early 19th Century
Water-colour, 8 by 10cm., framed
£100–130

Buckeridge (H.A.) A set of 6 humorous illustrations depicting the misfortunes of an angler stung by bees, ? executed in early 19th Century. Water-colour, 8 by 10 cm., framed £170

16.
Acknowledgements

British Bee Books IBRA 1979
History of beekeeping in Britain. H.Malcolm Fraser 1958
Understanding book collecting Grant Uden 1982
Book collecting as a hobby P.H. Muir 1945
Descriptive catalogue of a Library of bee-books Lt. Col. H.J.O. Walker 1929
Apicultural literature published in Canada and the United States
Johansson & Johansson 1972
Beemasters of the past Victor Dodd 1983
Book values and the book market N. Comben 1982
Book conservation Judith Jackson 1982
Bibliography for collectors Eric J. Freeman...... 1983
IBRA International Book Catalogue.
Sotheby's - Use of photograph - Page 48 and extracts from sale catalogues.

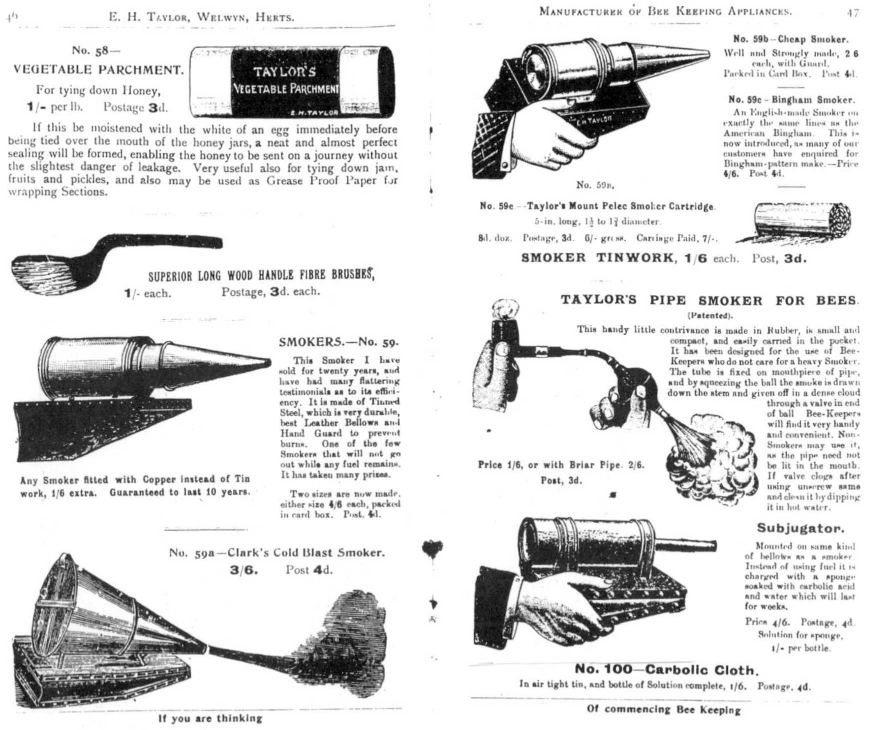

46 E. H. TAYLOR, WELWYN, HERTS.

No. 58—
VEGETABLE PARCHMENT.
For tying down Honey,
1/- per lb. Postage 3d.

If this be moistened with the white of an egg immediately before being tied over the mouth of the honey jars, a neat and almost perfect sealing will be formed, enabling the honey to be sent on a journey without the slightest danger of leakage. Very useful also for tying down jam, fruits and pickles, and also may be used as Grease Proof Paper for wrapping Sections.

SUPERIOR LONG WOOD HANDLE FIBRE BRUSHES,
1/- each. Postage, 3d. each.

SMOKERS.—No. 59.

This Smoker I have sold for twenty years, and have had many flattering testimonials as to its efficiency. It is made of Tinned Steel, which is very durable, best Leather Bellows and Hand Guard to prevent burns. One of the few Smokers that will not go out while any fuel remains. It has taken many prizes.

Two sizes are now made, either size 4/6 each, packed in card box. Post. 4d.

Any Smoker fitted with Copper instead of Tin work, 1/6 extra. Guaranteed to last 10 years.

No. 59a—Clark's Cold Blast Smoker.
3/6. Post 4d.

If you are thinking

MANUFACTURER OF BEE KEEPING APPLIANCES. 47

No. 59b—Cheap Smoker.
Well and Strongly made, 2/6 each, with Guard.
Packed in Card Box. Post 4d.

No. 59c – Bingham Smoker.
An English-made Smoker on exactly the same lines as the American Bingham. This is now introduced, as many of our customers have enquired for Bingham-pattern make.—Price 4/6. Post 4d.

No. 59B.

No. 59e—Taylor's Mount Pelee Smoker Cartridge.
5-in. long, 1½ to 1¾ diameter.
8d. doz. Postage, 3d. 6/- gross. Carriage Paid, 7/-.

SMOKER TINWORK, 1/6 each. Post, 3d.

TAYLOR'S PIPE SMOKER FOR BEES.
(Patented).

This handy little contrivance is made in Rubber, is small and compact, and easily carried in the pocket. It has been designed for the use of Bee-Keepers who do not care for a heavy Smoker. The tube is fixed on mouthpiece of pipe, and by squeezing the ball the smoke is drawn down the stem and given off in a dense cloud through a valve in end of ball Bee-Keepers will find it very handy and convenient. Non-Smokers may use it, as the pipe need not be lit in the mouth. If valve clogs after using unscrew same and clean it by dipping it in hot water.

Price 1/6, or with Briar Pipe. 2/6.
Post, 3d.

Subjugator.

Mounted on same kind of bellows as a smoker. Instead of using fuel it is charged with a sponge soaked with carbolic acid and water which will last for weeks.

Price 4/6. Postage, 4d.
Solution for sponge,
1/- per bottle.

No. 100—Carbolic Cloth.
In air tight tin, and bottle of Solution complete, 1/6. Postage, 4d.

Of commencing Bee Keeping

From Taylor's catalogue – smokers for sale.

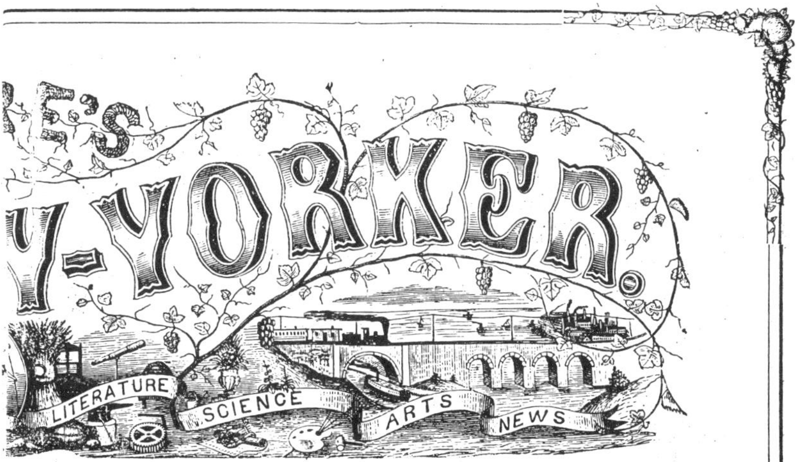

ROVEMENT." [SINGLE NO. FOUR CENTS.

DING SATURDAY, MARCH 1, 1862. {WHOLE NO. 633.

English required
ıad no fences, but
ogs were kept con-
large. Mr. R. (in
R.,) stated that not
ty kept a Shepherd
a visit among the
of Vermont. Mr.
heep men, had no
ıot see one in Ver-

hought the greatest
eir deterring people
nds were prevented
ıson. The sheep of
l in a few years on
logs among flocks,
ties, rendering the
ardous and unsafe,

sheep of this State
hin the past twenty
79 sheep; but five
ıer was reduced to
years the decrease
the census showed
has probably been
e 1855.

he resolutions were
scussion was inter-
t, and we regret our
d report. Could it
s of the Legislature,
ng dogs would not
rable body.

AL NOTES.

items in my note

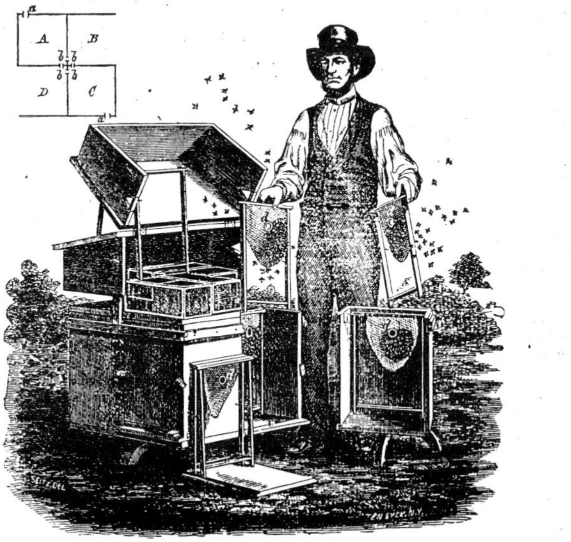

METCALF'S IMPROVED BEE-HIVE.

THE general attention now given to bee-culture, affords us great pleasure. This interest has been too much neglected, and if we have a little excitement and fever on the subject, of which speculators

stock swarm, C, transferring a comb frame precisely in the same manner before described, in this case to D, starting another small colony, and to this latter we attach one of the queen cells taken from B. We

What the papers said, New York State, 1862.

17.
Parting Words

"I have now said my say. Much good may it do you, which I am sure it will, if you give it a fair trial.

READ IT OFTEN; KEEP IT SAFE; LEND IT TO YOUR NEIGHBOURS WHO DO NOT KEEP BEES; TALK IT OVER WITH THOSE WHO DO; LEARN FROM THE BEE TO WORK HARD AND WASTE NOTHING. REMEMBER, NOTHING WORTH DOING CAN BE DONE WITHOUT A LITTLE TROUBLE; AND, ABOVE ALL, HELP EACH OTHER ALL YOU CAN

So goodbye to you.

GOD SAVE THE QUEEN"

Advice quoted from 'My bee book' by W. C. Cottton in his 'Letter to cottagers' – ? appropriate for collectors.

	The Bee Authors	*Literary Figures*	*Historical Events*
1400	Manuscripts	Chaucer - 'Canterbury	
		Tales'	1448 Gutenberg printing
			1477 Caxton pioneers
			1485 Tudors
1500	Fitzherbert 23		
	Tusser 57		
	Hill 68	Spenser - 'Fairie Queen'	Henry VII
	Heresbach 77		Henry VIII
1600	Southerne 93	Shakespeare - 'Hamlet'	Elizabeth, Armada 1588
	Butler 09		1603 Stuarts
	Markham 14		James I
	Bacon 27		
	Levett 34		1638 Bees taken to America
	Remnant 37	Milton - 'Paradise Lost'	1642-52 Civil War
	Hartlib 55		Commonwealth -
	Purchase 57		Oliver Cromwell
	Pepys 63		1660 Restoration - Charles II
	Evelyn 65		
	Hooke 65		
	Worlidge 69		
	Swammerdam 73		
	Gedde 75	Bunyan - 'Pilgrims Progress'	
	Rusden 79		
	Wheler 82		
	Dryden 97		
1700		Pope	1702 Queen Anne
	Warder 12		1714 George I
	Laurence 26		
	Bazin 44	Swift - 'Gullivers Travels'	
	Thorley 44		
	Maxwell 47		
	Hale 56	Dr Johnson - 'Dictionary'	
	S. White 56		Industrial Revolution
	T. Wildman 68	Capability Brown –	to 1830
	W. White 71	– landscape gardening	
	D. Wildman 73		
	Keys 80	Oliver Goldsmith	1783 American Independence
	Bonner 89	Gilbert White - 'Selbourne'	
	Huber 92	Wordsworth	1795 Revolutionary and
	Western Apiarian Soc 99		Napoleonic wars
1800	Kirby 02	Byron	to
	Huish 15	Jane Austen	1815 Waterloo
	Bevan 27	Cobbett	
	Gelieu 29		Great Reform Bill
	Nutt 32		
	Bagster 34		
	Taylor 38	Dickens - 'Pickwick'	1837 Queen Victoria
	Jardine 40		
	Cotton 42		
	Milton 43		
	Miner 49	Bronte sisters - 'Jane Eyre'	
	LANGSTROTH		Chartists
	Wood 53		1851 Great Exhibition
	Tegetmeier 60	Darwin - 'Origin of Species'	
	Woodbury 62		
	Neighbour 65	Tennyson	
	Pettigrew 70	George Eliot	1870 Elementary
	Cheshire 73	Browning	Education Act
	Hunter 75		
	BBKA 80		
	W. B. Carr 80		
	Cowan 81		
	Blow 82		
	Dzierzon 82		
	Lubbock 82	Thomas Hardy	
	Cheshire 86		
	Simmins 87		
1900	Maeterlinck 01	Kipling	Edward VII
	Digges 04	H. G. Wells	
	Edwardes 05		
	Fabre 11		George V
	Geary 11		
	Herrod-Hempsall 11	Rupert Brooke	
	Sladen 12		
	Mace 21	T. S. Eliot	First Great War